FULLY ALIVE

experiencing the
FIVE PILLARS of WHOLENESS

D1255465

What People Are Saying:

It gives me great joy to write the commentary for *"Fully Alive: Experiencing the Five pillars of Wholeness"*, written by Dr. Ademola Adewale. As a board-certified and licensed mental health counselor whose philosophy to healthcare is a holistic one, I believe that this timely and practical book written through the lens and lived experiences of Dr. Adewale will be relatable to not only physicians but professionals in any discipline. It will speak to each reader's heart, mind, and spirit to allow them to create a visual in their minds about what is occurring when reading it. Its messages of "Heal Thyself First" and "To Thy Own Self Be True," remind the reader that to be fully present for oneself, those they serve, their family, and society overall: they must be holistically well. I often tell people that the body, mind, and spirit are connected. If one or more of those subsystems is out of sync, it throws off the entire system's equilibrium, and Dr. Adewale eloquently conveyed this message in his book. The book will remind, inspire, and encourage all readers to take an inventory of their lives and adjust as needed to preserve themselves while living a healthy and balanced life.

—Letitia Browne-James, Ph.D., LMHC-S, NCC

FULLY ALIVE

experiencing the

FIVE PILLARS of WHOLENESS

Ademola Adewale, MD.

Another Quality Book Published By:
LEGACY BOOK PUBLISHING
1883 Lee Road, Winter Park, FL 32789
www.LEGACYBOOKPUBLISHING.com

Fully Alive:
Experiencing the Five Pillars of Wholeness

Published by:
LEGACY Book Publishing
1883 Lee Road
Winter Park, Florida 32789
www.LegacyBookPublishing.com

©2022 Ademola Adewale
ISBN: 978-1-947718-91-3
Printed in the United States, Second Printing

Cover Design by Gabriel H. Vaughn

Dedication

This book is dedicated to all the frontline ER doctors and physicians that lost their battle with Covid-19; those still suffering from the sequelae of Covid-19; and all those still in the trenches with me (ER docs, ER RNs, ED Techs, Respiratory therapists, and ER housekeepers) and all other frontline providers. Rest assured; this too shall pass eventually.

Acknowledgment

To my wife Tasha for embarking on this journey with me, encouraging me to complete this project, and providing me with a tranquil environment while juggling our three children (Adelana, Adara, and Ademola). You are deeply loved and appreciated.

To Robert Stephens at Story Impact Media for all your recommendations with the structure and invaluable advice. You are appreciated.

To Kathy Gibney Ph.D., for your insights and guidance.

To Herdley Paolini Ph.D., for your guidance, support, and mentorship over the years.

Table of Contents

Introduction

The Plight of an ER Doctor

I am Emergency Medicine. It lives in my blood, and it is what made and molded me into what I have become. I am a leader—resilient, innovative, dynamic, forward-thinking, unwavering amid adversities, and I possess what my late mentor Dr. Lasalle Leffall often referred to as "equanimity under duress." Simply speaking, under stress, I remained calm, cool, and unfazed. These are the absolute attributes of a true Emergency Medicine Physician. These qualities give Emergency Physicians the aura of invincibility, a kind of badass bravado that screams, "Bring it on!"

Every shift in the emergency department is dynamic, and no two days are the same. The adrenaline and the calmness you feel when you hear trauma code red, or a cardiac arrest en route to the ER is intoxicating. The joy you feel with successful resuscitation of that sick patient, and the thrill of delivering that baby in the ER molds the Emergency Physician. Additionally, the solemnness and humility you experience from the loss of the patient you did not expect to succumb that overwhelm you when delivering the bad news to that parent whose only child was killed by a drive-by shooting on Christmas eve; these are the scenarios that shape the Emergency Physicians to develop the intestinal fortitude to withstand the challenges of the profession.

As an Emergency Medicine Physician evolves in the career of being a frontline physician, that once-young invincible, badass, unfazed physician is now in a meaningful relationship, or married with kids, involved in the community—little league baseball, basketball, or soccer coach—and is now responsible for others' well-being in an entirely different way, unlike his emergency department patients. The perspectives changes, gravitating towards more leadership or administrative roles, and the operating mantra begins to mirror risk aversion, with waning excitement for the so-called adrenaline charging scenarios. The aura of invincibility starts to dissipate slowly.

As the aura of invincibility begins to wane, the incessant regulations both federally and institutionally, as well as the loss of autonomy, render us bare. We are not as invincible as we thought. When these issues were compounded with the trends of Venture Capitalist companies acquiring independent physician group practices over the past decade, respected physicians began to view themselves as mere dispensable workhorses for the Wall Street juggernauts. Most felt completely marginalized without any voice and had lost the complete autonomy they cherished in their respective group practices.

As if this were not tough enough on the physician's psyche and morale, the arrival of the Covid-19 pandemic was a game-changer. The marginalized, undervalued, burned-out physicians with low morale were now faced with battling a pandemic that is ravaging the communities we serve- what a way to add an accelerant to a simmering fire. Although we are usually prepared to meet any challenges head-on, we felt incapacitated, unprepared, and unprotected by the sheer lack of basic supplies needed to protect ourselves and the patients we serve from the unforgiving disease.

As many of us contemplated reusing disposable masks until they were soiled, some were unfortunate enough to contract the disease and ended up in a precarious medical situation. The lack of plausible therapy earlier in the game led to the demise of several outstanding and beloved clinicians. Those fortunate to survive the disease were traumatized and suffered silently as a Covid-19 long-hauler and from post-Covid-19 anxiety symptoms.

As earlier elucidated, even before Covid, a lot of physicians and healthcare providers were struggling with burn-out, moral injury, or near depression as a result of the undue burden of being a healthcare provider in this era. Then came the stress of treating

Covid-19 patients, the constant fear of potentially becoming infected with the virus and dying from it, and the concerns of taking the virus home to our loved ones was particularly overwhelming and debilitating.

Personally, at one point, I felt so impotent and was unable to render any meaningful therapy to struggling and potentially dying patients. This severely traumatized me to the point that I almost walked away from medicine at the peak of the pandemic. I was physically exhausted, mentally fatigued, and emotionally drained. I struggled with sleepless nights as any attempt to shutter my eyes conjured nightmarish images of myself on a ventilator and dying from the disease I was trying to treat. I constantly worried for my family and loved ones, and I constantly struggled with the idea of walking away from medicine entirely. I was nearing depression, was morally injured, and suffering from what I called Covid-19 anxiety and fatigue symptoms and a sense of failure. This was the lowest point for me.

The idea of walking away from my colleagues in the trenches during the peak of a pandemic is tantamount to abandonment, irrespective of how I felt personally. Here lies the quagmire. While I quietly struggled with fear and anxiety, I continued to care for the patients I swore to protect, maximized the protection afforded to me by my institution that invested at least a billion dollars in resources, developed coping skills to the new normal, and just tried to stay alive and relevant as we battled the pandemic.

The arrival of the vaccine was a game-changer. The day I received my first dose was the first time in a year that I was able to exhale. Also, that evening, I was able to have a very deserved good night's sleep without the ventilator nightmare. The fear of contracting the virus began to slowly dissipate with the assumption that even if I contracted the virus, it couldn't kill me. I may get sick, but I would be just fine. This is powerful. I can now proceed with caring for my patients with renewed hope for the future of battling the pandemic and life returning to some kind of semblance of normalcy.

Although we have turned the corner in the battle against Covid-19, this is an Eschar on the underlying wounds that were sustained before the pandemic and even worsened by it. Now is the time for us healthcare providers to start refocusing on ourselves. It is time for us to exhale and heal our wounds, minds, bodies,and spirits. If we have to continue on this journey and sustain the house of medicine, we have to collectively embark on the journey to be whole.

The journey to wholeness requires some intentionality. Starting the process requires a unique understanding of how healthcare providers slowly and quietly arrived at the state of burnout, mental exhaustion, colloquial depression, and unspoken mental health crisis in medicine.

This book will take you through this journey from the lens of a frontline provider while meandering through the intricate state of our current healthcare system, the changes that need to occur, the psychological impact of the current system on our healthcare providers (physicians, nurses, administrators, ancillary staff, and anyone involved the industry), and the road to healing and redemption.

By the time you complete reading this book, my goal is to provide you with a clear understanding of the current state of our healthcare system, and dilemmas encountered by healthcare providers, and how to begin your journey to become Fully Alive using the Five Pillars of Wholeness. Additionally, I hope to provide you with tools that will allow you to attain the closest semblance to life balance and develop the intestinal fortitude to meet any challenges that life brings your way.

Chapter One

The Unraveling of the House of Medicine

Should the house of medicine be allowed to go on life support?

Over the past decade, the attributes that attracted me to this profession (humanity; compassion; empathy; humility; self-confidence; honesty; effective communication; its graceful, respectful, respectable, and professional nature; and the aura of the profession itself) are now becoming an Achille's heel. The humanity in you is constantly used as a weapon to take advantage of you, and your compassion is waning to the extent that we now use the term "compassion fatigue." The empathy you displayed is now utilized as a tool to guilt-trip you, and your humility oftentimes is perceived as weakness and taken advantage of until you become outspoken. The self-confidence you demonstrate is constantly questioned by bureaucrats pushing protocols that have no bearing on what you do. The respect you have garnered as a physician is now a source of scorn by the people you are trying to care for, and the aura of the profession itself is becoming anathema to the people who practice the profession.

How did we get here? The bureaucratic nightmare! Regulations after regulations that impede the autonomy of the profession. The simplest tasks are like performing a proctologic exam with many layers of mundane processes. Learned professionals are now glorified paper pushers spending more time performing nonsensical tasks instead of focusing on patient care. The love for the profession continues to wane as dignified physicians forego medicine entirely after years of incessant bombardment that erodes their patience, which inadvertently leads to burnout, or what is now commonly referred to as moral injury. I was once deeply in love with medicine, but my love slowly waned and required some soul searching.

Let me take a moment here to discuss the phenomenon called "moral injury." What is it? It is a term that has recently been utilized in the military to describe crises faced by soldiers enduring internal suffering because of carrying out activities that violate their moral code. Suffice it to say; it is tantamount to a wound to the conscience, anguishing soul, or a broken spirit. This right here is what most physicians or healthcare providers are feeling these days. Healthcare providers feel that they have lost their moral compass as it relates to the autonomy in caring for their patients.

The pressure to consistently meet demands that are sometimes construed as unfair to the patients (such as early discharges when they think the patient is not ready to be discharged or creating barriers to readmission if a patient returns in less than thirty days), demands to see patients at the speed of light while requesting the providers to address all salient concerns of the patients for the purpose of metrics and accolades, and the so-called metrics attached to compensation or incentives. All these competing demands put healthcare providers in the middle. They have lost autonomy—broken, overworked, and often morally bankrupt in an incessant effort to meet the demands of the current healthcare state.

Circling back, how do I rediscover the meaning in medicine in this metrics-driven environment and amidst the constant conflicts between competing regulations? As we struggle with D2D (Door to Discharge), here comes "Patient-Centered Care" or "Whole-Patient Care." In essence, speed now becomes paramount to care while concomitantly imploring physicians to take the time to address all the patient's concerns. The two cannot exist in the same universe. While I routinely practice Whole-Patient Care, oftentimes, the drive to meet the metrics is a barrier. I watch clinicians struggle with this, and I have seen a few walk away from the field due to burnout or transition to concierge medicine services.

As I tried to find meaning in the metrics-driven arena, it dawned on me that healthcare providers are burning out or becoming morally injured because of the overwhelming demands. This leads me to the question: How can a healthcare provider practice Whole-Patient or Patient-Centered Care when they are not whole or centered themselves or are morally injured? A provider that is not whole and is about to unravel is not in any shape to survive in this current state of medicine.

As physicians continue to deal with burnout in significant proportions, some suffer from either colloquial or clinical depression. Simultaneously, hospital leaderships, administrators, or the so-called C-suite management members keep echoing the sentiments that physicians are not resilient enough and they need resilience training. Unbeknownst to them is the quiet undertone of mental health crises in medicine, with about three to four hundred physicians committing suicide each year.[1,2,3,4,5,6] The pervasiveness of an under-reported crisis that percolates through the walls of hospital systems affecting doctors, nurses, allied health providers, and ancillary team members is like embers waiting for propellants to start the next wildfire. And then came the Covid-19 pandemic!

The arrival of Covid-19 on our shores was the propellant the embers needed to become the next raging wildfire. The physicians that are currently overworked, drowning in the barrage of bureaucratic nightmares, and tethering on the edge of burnout or already burned out are about to be embroiled in a situation beyond their control that will lead to the rapid removal of the veil from the face of mental health crises in health care.

As the northeast of the United States suffered from the early onslaught of battling the disease, stories from colleagues on the frontlines were initially hard to comprehend until vivid images started circulating on social media and personal accounts from friends and colleagues in the line of fire. The lack of protective devices needed for personal protection while dealing with this deluge was unbelievable. The clogged hospital hallway beds and the insurmountable number of deaths with dead bodies piling up in hospital morgues and makeshift refrigerators on hospital grounds sent a disconcerting message to all frontline providers.

While ruminating over the situation and wondering why this was happening, I started fielding notifications about colleagues who had contracted the disease and the ones who had unfortunately succumbed to their illness. Simultaneously, the ones still standing continued to work tirelessly to provide whatever little care they could afford the sick while quietly battling their own anguish, anxiety, and internal turmoil of potentially becoming the next victim. Spending countless nights consoling and comforting colleagues to hang in there while they worked endless shifts reusing protective gear that could potentially expose them to infections was overwhelming. Quietly, I wondered when my tsunami would arrive or when my embers would turn into a raging wildfire.

As we contemplated the quagmire in medicine and the undue burden on healthcare providers, the whole world began to unravel with the coronavirus pandemic. The world today is strongly interconnected. This interconnectedness creates an environment that allows for easy transmission of communicable diseases over thousands of miles. The communicable diseases that have evolved over the past two decades are more virulent and often evolve into an epidemic or pandemic. The Severe Acute Respiratory Distress Syndrome (SARS) outbreak in 2003, the Middle Eastern Respiratory Distress Syndrome (MERS) in 2012, and Ebola in 2014 were all epidemic conditions. Presently, Covid-19 is a pandemic of devastating proportions. As all these diseases evolve, healthcare providers are thrust into the frontline of caring for the population infected with these diseases.

Healthcare providers deal with clear and present dangers on a daily basis. However, dealing with dangers that are clearly visible is one thing; dealing with dangers that are not quite discernible but deadly is a different story entirely. The current Covid-19 pandemic is an example of a danger that cannot be visualized. Simply put, the virus cannot be visualized, sniffed, or perceived. If you are unfortunate to contract the virus as a healthcare provider, the consequences could be devastating. Here lies the paradigm shift. Throughout our career, the superb aura of equanimity under duress, the uncanny ability to make order out of chaos, and the incessant ability to be solution-oriented have defined most healthcare providers. But now, we are dealing with situations where we are rendered impotent because of the limitations of what we could really offer to those afflicted with the Covid-19 virus.

Presently, the battle we are fighting on the frontlines has unfortunately taken the lives of some of our friends and colleagues, stricken several others with long-lasting sequelae, and the remainder—

while still standing—continue to selflessly care for the afflicted while quietly pondering the potential inevitability of contracting the virus. For once, as a healthcare provider, I am scared, and the anxiety of potentially contaminating myself is emotionally draining. The anxiety we deal with compounded by Covid-19 fatigue and Covid-19 anxiety symptoms is overwhelming, and we are all trying to navigate our way out of this current environment.

Why are we so exposed and our healthcare systems challenged and overwhelmed in this pandemic? Well, steps that needed to be taken to ensure adequate mitigation were ignored earlier in the crisis by those who could affect changes. Consequently, healthcare workers were left exposed and unprepared in the context of protective devices that protect us from the unseen agent we are trying to treat while saving lives. We were left with inadequate tools to help us perform our job effectively. Inadvertently, we became victims of the disease that we were trying to battle. As stated earlier, while some of our colleagues succumbed to the disease, the remaining are now dealing with silent mental health crises that are the culmination of where we were before Covid-19, the anguish of caring for Covid-19 patients, Covid-19 anxieties, and fatigue symptoms brought upon us.

The moral injury we were initially dealing with was nothing compared to its escalation in the era of Covid-19. The incessant decision-making as to who to send home or keep in the hospital despite knowing that either option might be futile was unnerving. We are forced to make these decisions due to the lack of capacity to accommodate the needs of the community. Additionally, some decisions we have had to make are almost tantamount to rationing. For example, having to determine who receives ventilator support or ECMO (extracorporeal membrane oxygenation) to treat the Covid-19 virus that is overwhelming their systems, or denying families the ability to see their loved ones for the last time, or determining who gets the supposedly life-saving drugs that are in short supply. Healthcare providers are feeling overwhelmingly morally injured and need an intervention. While some have unfortunately committed suicide, more are silently suffering, just like military personnel on the frontline carrying out directives that conflict with their moral ethos.

How do providers thrive in the current medical environment? Spare me the resilience jargon. Just prior to Covid-19, the conversation was evolving toward physician resilience—they are not resilient enough. That is sheer nonsensical talk. The core to survival for every clinician known to me is resilience. You cannot make it through medical school and the arduous and sometimes atrocious residency training without being resilient. While in medical school, I recall the sayings: "equanimity under duress," "tightening your sphincter tone," and "take it like a man." To be resilient is not a choice; it's a learned behavior throughout medical school and residencies. It is one of the fundamental attributes you acquire during training.

(Footnotes)

[1] Frédéric Dutheil et al., "Suicide among Physicians and Health-Care Workers."

[2] Molly C Kalmoe et al., "Physician Suicide: A Call to Action."

[3] Christine Yu Moutier et al., "Preventing Clinician Suicide."

[4] Amanda M Kingston, "Break the Silence."

[5] Leslie Kane, "Medscape's 2020 Physician Burnout Report."

[6] Eva S. Schernhammer and Graham A. Colditz, "Suicide Rates among Physicians."

Chapter Two

The Pandemic of the Unvaccinated

Disabling shock to the bedrock of the system.

The Covid-19 pandemic created a devastating crisis in the healthcare system. The unspoken part of the crisis the population never gets to experience or appreciate. Presently, most hospital systems have significant manpower shortages that resulted from the multiple phases of the pandemic. Hospitals cannot operate without the availability of nurses. Although the physicians create treatment plans, the nurses must execute them. The nurses are at the bedside of all our patients, making sure that all their care needs are delivered effectively and efficiently. The nurses are the integral fabric of our intricate healthcare system. They are the bedrock of our healthcare infrastructure. Without the nurses, no hospital system can function.

Current emphasis portrays burnout, depression, compassion fatigue, and moral injury among physicians while ignoring similar if not worse impacts on the nurses. The recurrent waves of the surge in Covid-19 infections accelerated the emotional anguish and burnout equally suffered by our nurses. Most of our nurses were already exiting the field to become nurse practitioners or certified registered nurse anesthetists due to the overwhelming demands and unending stress of the job of being a nurse (can you see the parallelism of trends with physicians?). The unbearable number of sufferings and deaths witnessed by the nurses during the first, second, and third waves of the pandemic is enough to cause anyone to suffer from post-traumatic stress disorder. The nurses spend the most time with the isolated Covid patients; they conduct all the teleconferences via iPads with the families and loved ones of the dying covid patients. They are often the last healthcare contact to the patients before they succumb to their illness. To add to that nightmare, they are the ones that assist in transferring the deceased bodies into body bags.

Can you envision the trauma such experiences would cause anyone? Can you imagine the gravity and the emotional toll of going through the above routine several times during the day, weeks, or months? Well, that was, and still is, the ordeal of our nurses. Many of the nurses that underwent the above experiences suffered significant emotional trauma. While several unfortunately committed suicide, some became severely depressed, some walked away from the field of nursing, and a lot took a long sabbatical to address their mental health. The few remaining continued to staff our hospitals in an overworked capacity.

Though hospitals were short-staffed, the transient break in the resurgence of Covid-19 with the wide availability of the vaccine was a welcoming relief. This lull allowed hospitals to catch up on caring for non-Covid-19 patients with the anticipation of a potential return to some sort of new normal. The nurses were working harder than normal, and most understood the shortages and leveraged that to enhance their compensations.

Although the hospitals were willing to accommodate the expenses incurred from the bidding wars for limited pools of nurses to staff hospital beds, the fear of how to manage another potential surge or rise in the cases of infected Covid-19 patients was palpable in the hallways of hospitals.

The mission to vaccinate the entire population so that we can attain herd immunity, and proceed with our new normal, was made more urgent by the ravages of the delta variant of the Covid-19 virus in India, and other parts of the world, and the inevitability of similar trends on our shores. However, the incessant effort of the saboteurs of the success of the pace of vaccination through conspiracy theories created a wave of vaccine hesitancy and the rise of the so-called anti-vaccination movement.

With increasing vaccine hesitancy and the impending apocalyptic consequences, the hospitals started raising the alarm. The hospitals understood the gravity of the consequences of new surges in Covid cases because they were severely handicapped by staffing shortages and incapable of meeting the demands of the potential inundation with critically ill Covid patients. The campaigns to get vaccinated were ignored, and slowly, as predicted, we started seeing trickles of the unvaccinated showing up in the hospitals. This eventually evolved into a flood of sick unvaccinated Covid patients that has catapulted into what we now refer to as the "pandemic of the unvaccinated."

The so-called pandemic of the unvaccinated is totally inexcusable. The idea that as a country, we allowed our toxic political divide (that pitched blue against red and elimination of the middle) to percolate into our public health policy in a time of crisis is insane. People allowed their allegiance and fealty to a political party and leaders and fidelity to an ideology to override their own intuitions and ability to discern what's right from wrong. Consequently, people subject themselves to embracing conspiracy theories that declared the coronavirus pandemic a hoax and referred to the developed vaccines to tackle the pandemic as a governmental device to track the population. The wealth and sophistication of the disinformation, paralleled with the willful ignorance to embrace them, has led to the vaccination hesitancy that is now pervasive in our communities.[7]

The hesitancy among a political group along a party line, and those who subjected themselves to embracing the disinformation, is now driving the resurgence in the pandemic that we are currently dealing with. The vaccine hesitancy led to the inability to accomplish the so-called herd immunity and allowed the emergence of the delta variant mutation. Presently, the majority of the severely ill Covid patients that are inundating the hospitals are unvaccinated, younger, and often believed the pandemic was a hoax and did not trust the vaccines. Ironically, those same people that do not trust the vaccines are willing to receive experimental treatments that are not fully approved when they are gravely ill. One nurse in Louisiana, Bren Ingle said: "Ninety-nine percent of the patients being admitted are unvaccinated. They're sicker when they get here. They require more acute care while they're here. And unfortunately, many of them are not surviving." This mirrors my own experience. She summed up my thoughts perfectly as a frontline worker in this pandemic: "It's extremely frustrating, the ignorance of people not getting the vaccine because they don't believe in it, or they don't think it'll help them. You have the chance to get them. They're free. And people still refuse."[8]

The irony here is unbelievable. You have a subset of the population that believed in the theory that the vaccines to curtail the devastating effects of infection with the delta variant are governmental apparatuses used to track and control the population, or that the pace of the vaccine's development was corrupted and financially driven, or that even the FDA has not fully approved the vaccines. These same people are willing and requesting to be infused with the non-FDA-approved experimental treatments when afflicted with the virus. To add insult to this sheer madness, this same subset of the population that refuses to be vaccinated is also refusing to embrace the simplest preventive modality: wearing a mask.

The ideological divide here is perplexing. The theory that the prevention of a disease is better and cheaper than the cure has been dismissed or shunned by purported willful ignorance and blind allegiance to some spurious ideology or beliefs. Consequently, leaders that were supposed to be promoting preventive modalities are embracing and promoting experimental treatments for members of the population that are infected with the virus. This oxymoronic idea that it's okay to ignore disease-preventing modalities such as mask-wearing or getting vaccinated, but if you get infected, we have free experimental drugs for you is dumbfounding. This sheer willful ignorance or blatant disingenuity by influential leaders is the impetus behind our current quagmire: a pandemic of the unvaccinated.

Presently, the hallways of emergency departments nationwide are lined with sick patients as many of the hospital beds are currently occupied by unvaccinated Covid patients, especially with the new Delta variant. David Wohl, a specialist in infectious diseases at the University of North Carolina, said this in the *Washington Post*: "There is an incredible increase in hospitalizations across the spectrum, from just needing oxygen and some care to needing serious interventions to keep people alive. If everyone was vaccinated, our hospitals would not be anywhere near where we are."[9]

Most hospitals are seeing two to three times the volume of Covid patients compared to prior phases at similar times in 2020. Hospitals all over the country are almost at capacity with severe shortages of nurses, ancillary service members, and even critical care and emergency medicine physicians. Admitted patients are spending days in the emergency departments all over the country with no hope of being transferred to inpatient beds. Emergency departments are flooded with hallway beds for the care of both Covid and non-Covid patients, ambulances are waiting for an extended duration to offload sick patients transferred to the hospitals, and there is a paucity of beds in the emergency room to care for critically sick emergent patients. Consequently, the care of critically ill non-Covid patients is now being compromised by the flood of unvaccinated Covid patients. Patients with chronic health conditions, those needing specialty care, or cancer patients that needed surgeries are now witnessing delays in their care because of a lack of hospital beds.

The pandemic of the unvaccinated is a totally avoidable healthcare disaster. The cataclysmic effects on the system will be felt for years to come. Let me put this in perspective. The healthcare system was already short-staffed with a significantly small labor pool of nurses to tap from. The currently available nurses are overstretched and overworked to the extent that extra financial incentives have no effect. However, the hospitals are inundated with barrages of critically ill unvaccinated Covid patients with limited capacities to take care of them. Although there may be available hospital beds, there is a paucity of nursing and ancillary personnel to staff the units. Here lies the current quagmire.

The nurses, doctors, and other team members are overworked and tired. The recurrent theme of the conversations in hospital hallways is that this is completely avoidable. The frustration of going through this phase of the pandemic is palpable on the faces of most healthcare workers and it is turning compassion into resentment. Physicians and healthcare workers are now suffering from what I refer to as "healthcare workers resentment syndrome." Some physicians are now refusing to care for patients that are not vaccinated, basically instructing such patients not to show up at their practice facility. The blame for the current situation is squarely directed toward the unvaccinated.[10]

As the volume of unvaccinated ill patients continues to escalate, care teams are now thrust once again into an ethical dilemma. With the lack of nurses to staff intensive care beds, and the overall lack of available intensive care beds, tough decisions must be made regarding which patient receives any available ventilator. This means that some patients will die needlessly because of the lack of services that could potentially extend or save their lives. Lifesaving and sustaining treatments using the "ECMO" (extracorporeal membrane oxygenation) for the severely ill unvaccinated Covid-19 patients now must be rationed. To utilize this service requires a one-to-one intensive care nurse that is not available. The usual ratio of an intensive care nurse to two patients is now being stretched to a single nurse to three or even four patients to maximize the capacity of the available beds. The overwhelming stress and demands of this arrangement on the critical care nurses are further leading to rapid exit from the pool of available high-demand critical care nurses. The effects of these exits will further diminish the number of available intensive care beds, and severely ill patients requiring intensive care beds will have nowhere to go and will be stuck in the emergency departments.

As if things were not bad enough, the moral injury sustained by the specialists that determine which of the dying patients on the ventilator should be placed on the ECMO treatments will also have a long-lasting effect. Can you imagine having to decide which patient lives or dies? Can you comprehend the emotional toll on the physician that knows for sure that he or she can provide these services and has the machines to provide this life-saving treatment but is incapable of accomplishing this task because of the lack of staff? In essence, some patients that could have benefitted from the lifesaving and sustaining treatments will die needlessly. The consequences of this on the physician are the suffrage of moral injury and potential depression, and post-traumatic stress disorder.

Due to the fact that the dire situation the healthcare system is currently dealing with is avoidable, the emotional toll sustained by healthcare workers is negatively affecting the sentiments towards the unvaccinated. The compassion that represents the essence of all or most healthcare workers, which has now been accelerated into compassion fatigue due to the deluge of unvaccinated sick patients, has now been replaced by resentment. The "healthcare workers resentment syndrome" is worsening by the minute, and the mentality of "why should I care for you if you refuse to care for yourself" is becoming more pronounced. The implication of resentment being expressed by healthcare workers toward the patient they are caring for is a new dimension that will have a lasting impact on the healthcare system as we continue to battle this pandemic. One doctor in Utah said, "I try to be fair. I know I'm a well-off white doctor who understands science and medicine. The vaccine came to my place of work, and I just rolled up my sleeve. I get that it's harder for other people. But at this point it's, like, c'mon, man, this is the most important thing you can do for your health. I'm frustrated, and I don't know what to do to make myself un-frustrated."[11]

The pandemic of the unvaccinated will re-shape our healthcare system for years to come. As we witness significant amounts of unnecessary deaths among the unvaccinated sick patients, a proportion of our remaining doctors, nurses, and ancillary team members will exit the field (that has already started due to the resentment syndrome), a lot of healthcare providers will suffer significant mental health crises that will take years to recover from. The healthcare system as a whole will suffer significant financial stress that will render some systems bankrupt or significantly limit the services, they provide to the communities they serve. Here lie the unintended consequences of the pandemic of the unvaccinated.

(Footnotes)
[7] "Anti-Vaxxers, Anti-Maskers and Conspiracists."

[8] Lev Facher, "Unvaccinated Deaths Overwhelm Health Workers in Covid Hot Zones."

[9] Frances Stead Sellers et al., "The Delta Variant Is Putting America's Hospitals Back in Crisis Mode."

[10] Michael A Smith, "We Don't Owe the Unvaccinated Priority on Hospital Care."

[11] Dhruv Khullar, "Treating the Unvaccinated."

Chapter Three

Salvaging the House of Medicine

Money sure is the root of all evil.

How many times have you heard the saying that the American healthcare system is broken? The system suffers from a chronic systemic disease that needs immediate intervention to stop the progression of its slow death. Policy experts and physicians often attribute these systemic problems to overwhelming bureaucratic regulations. Earlier in the book, I discussed the unraveling of the house of medicine and the bureaucratic nightmare that forces doctors and providers alike to perform mundane tasks that takes them away from patient care and devalue their autonomy. Now, let's take a look at the other side of the system.

While I will humbly not opine on the solution to the systemic problems in this book, as that will require a post-doctoral dissertation, I will at least attempt to shed some light on the main players in our current healthcare state. The big elephant in the room is money. The escalating costs of healthcare delivery in the United States, when compared to the rest of the world, are mind-boggling. This cost is a runaway train that needs to be slowed down. There are seven main players in this game: the federal government, hospitals, pharmaceutical companies, insurance companies, physicians, lawyers, and consumers. Each of these players plays a significant role in the cost of care.

The emphasis of this segment will be directed toward three of the main characters (the government, hospitals, and physicians).

The federal government is the main player in the game and the biggest spender. In 2019, the federal government expended 17.7 percent of the GDP on healthcare. Overall, the entire healthcare spending between all parties grew by 4.6 percent to a staggering $3.8 trillion. This equates to almost $11,582/person. Presently, it is projected that the national healthcare expenditure (NHE) will increase by an annual rate of 5.4 percent from 2019 to 2028 and reach $6.8 trillion by 2028.[12] This is not sustainable. When compared to other industrialized countries, our spending gap has gradually widened since 1960.[13, 14] These increasing costs and variabilities in the qualities of delivered care has made the reform of healthcare a cultural and political dilemma.

In an attempt by the government to control costs, several governmental oversight agencies were created. The main agency is the United States Department of Health and Human Services (HHS). This agency oversees the Center for Medicare and Medicaid Services (CMS) and is responsible for the administration of programs that protect the health of the population, including Medicare, Medicaid, the Marketplace, and the Children Health Insurance Program (CHIP). CMS regulates the reimbursements for healthcare products and services for the two largest healthcare programs in the country (Medicare and Medicaid). In essence, CMS holds the purse to the bulk of American healthcare. For CMS to curtail the escalating cost, it has to create several regulations and protocols that every participating hospital must meet to receive reimbursements for the services rendered. Here lies a problem.

Another important agency under the auspices of the HHS is the Agency for Healthcare Research and Quality (AHRQ). This is the lead agency responsible for supporting research designed to improve the quality of health care, increase access to essential services, and reduce the overall cost of the care delivered. For AHRQ to carry out its obligations, it also has to regulate. Here lies another problem.

The second player in the game is the hospital system. Hospitals are business entities that are either for-profit or not-for-profit. At the end of the day, the designations are all semantics because each still has to make money. The hospitals have to account for administrative expenditures, the cost of supplies, and wages and salaries.

According to the report from the commonwealth fund in 2014, the administrative cost accounts for twenty-five percent (roughly over $200 billion) of total hospital spending in the United States. However, outside of the United States, administrative costs usually represent three to five percent of the total cost. Let's put this in perspective for a minute here; this cost ranged from 1.43 percent of GDP in the United States ($667 per capita) when compared to 0.41 percent of GDP ($158 per capita) in Canada.[15] What does this cost entail? Well, they include marketing expenditure and overhead associated with administrative tasks, salaries for employees responsible for billing and coding, the administrative team that must negotiate multiple contracts with insurance companies, and the team that is responsible for the hospital regulatory and compliance. There lies a problem. Someone has to pay for these administrative expenses.

The costs of procuring supplies that hospitals utilize to provide the service they render continue to rise. Depending on the size of the hospital and the specialty services it provides, these costs could be astounding. This is evident in operating suites supplies. There are variations in costs and supplies utilized by surgeons to perform similar procedures. Without standardization of supplies, these exorbitant costs are passed on to the patients. Can you imagine two surgeons performing similar procedures, but one costs $10,000 while the other costs $50,000? When you take a deep dive into why such variations exist, you notice that the expensive surgeon utilized a plate that costs $15,000 apiece to secure a segment of a bone while the other surgeon utilized equally effective cheaper plates that cost less than $1,500 for a similar outcome.[16, 17]

The costs of wages to employees add up rapidly. With narrowing labor pools coupled with increasing demands, these costs will continue to increase. In different cities and states, hospitals are the largest labor employer. Hospitals employ people with myriads of skillsets, from doctors, nurses, and therapists, to janitorial, clerical, and food services. These employees are instrumental to the day-to-day operations of the hospital. With increasing regulations, in order to maintain compliances, the hospital has to hire and pay top-shelf wages to the compliance team. As we can see, hospitals spend a lot of money employing people. However, they also spend a lot more to stay compliant with the regulations. The more regulations, the more they have to spend on these subsets of employees.

As hospitals struggle to meet the increasing regulatory demands from both federal and state agencies and decrease reimbursements from insurance companies, they must engage in a dialogue with the physicians on how to curtail cost and decrease the variabilities in care. Here lies the number three player in the game: The physicians. For several years now, physicians have been the scapegoat of the rising cost of healthcare in the United States. Since physician's order and perform tests, many critics have blamed them for creating the current conundrum where the United States leads the world in health care expenditures.

Once again, as we discuss the role of physicians in this systemic failure, making money still stands out. Physicians also have to make money delivering care. The business of medicine is an interwoven quagmire. The physicians spend years becoming a doctor while accumulating thousands of dollars in educational debt. For the graduating class of 2019, the American Medical Association (AMA) indicated the average medical school debt was $201,490. Basically, most medical school graduates prior to residency training owe over two hundred thousand dollars and this does not account for undergraduate education debts. If this cost continues to rise unchecked, it is estimated that by 2024, the average medical school debt will exceed three hundred thousand dollars. This is sheer insanity.

As physicians began to practice medicine as either an employee or in a self-employed model, competing demands defined the practice style. The practice style of some physicians, if not many, is the unintended consequence of regulations. Imagine the scenario where a physician is incentivized to admit more patients to the hospital, discharge patients as soon as possible, or order more tests. These are real scenarios that have been widely reported. Every regulation that the government imposes is constantly countered by ways to maneuver around them. All the protocols and bundles that the regulatory bodies mandated the hospitals to follow are being passed down to the doctors to execute. Most of these bundles are fraught with wastes that are inadvertently perpetuated. If a physician fails to utilize these bundles, it affects their metrics, and the metrics affect their compensations. As you can see here, the unintended consequences are wastes which leads to increased cost of the care delivered. Here lies another problem. This is almost tantamount to a pay-to-play scheme unintendedly championed by the regulatory bodies.

Several regulations to curtail the escalating cost of care, such as but not limited to, the thirty days readmission, capitations, bundled payments, mandated transition to electronic medical records, and the electronic prescribing, all falls on the laps of the physicians. The penalty for lack of compliance in the form of decreased financial reimbursements impacts both the hospitals and the physicians.

Let's take, for example, the bundled payment. This is a model that is purported to advance value-based care by providing incentives to providers and hospitals to coordinate care for better outcomes, efficiency, quality, and decreased cost. In this model, healthcare facilities and providers are paid a single payment for all the services they perform to treat a patient undergoing a specific episode of care. The care delivery process within a period of time for a certain condition is referred to as an episode of care. This episode includes the entire continuum of care. The optics of this model looks good, but the devil is in the details. By virtue of the built-in capitations, the providers and the hospitals assume the risks of the extra cost incurred while simultaneously benefiting from the windfalls. The problem here is that the windfall rarely materializes because of the overwhelming numbers of complex patients with chronic medical conditions and those that are non-compliant with defined treatment pathways.

As you can see from the bundled payment example, the financial burden was shifted from the government to the hospitals or healthcare facilities and the providers. In order for the hospitals to stay in compliance with this, they have to invest significantly in manpower to police every aspect of the care-delivery process while simultaneously looking for ways to ensure financial solvency. Similar to the hospitals, the physicians have to expend significant time and workforce to minimize the financial impacts on their bottom line.

The overwhelming stress of balancing the exorbitant expenditure on administrative staff, maintaining compliance with all the regulations, trying to make a living while delivering quality care has an unintended consequence on physicians. Therefore, some physicians are burned out, depressed, and walking away from the profession they love, which has the potential side effect of neglecting and abandoning the patients that need their services. These subsets of physicians are just fed up with the whole system, and the perceived environment of a practice is not suitable for their quality of life or their psyche, as it handicaps them from freely performing the art of medicine.

In order to survive in the current healthcare environment, cunning ways are constantly being devised to mitigate against the overall effects of all the regulations. To remain financially solvent, some physicians may resort to gaming the system by avoiding high-risk patients, changing coding practices by upcoding to maximize reimbursements, or by moving services in time or location to qualify for separate reimbursements. Here lies another problem: The unintended consequences of the regulations.

The house of medicine is broken and heading towards life support. It needs a complete overhaul to revive it and keep it alive for the sake of the American people that will need the attention of the house of medicine at one time or the other in their lifetime. The escalating cost of care delivery in the United States is not sustainable and drastic changes must occur. While politicians are bickering over ideological differences, working on a comprehensive solution by engaging with all the players in the game as active participants should be the priority and the starting point. The current situation with competing financial interests among all the players, as well as more regulations, will not solve the problem. It will only cause the situation to deteriorate further.

Unfortunately, we cannot trust politicians or legislators to address the problem. Piecemeal reforms without addressing the elephant in the room are tantamount to putting lipstick on a pig. Policy experts from all the players and some of the players themselves have worked tirelessly on achieving a fair compromise to curtail costs, improve care quality, and make recommendations to the legislators. Until our legislators are truly serious about embarking on tough decisions (medical liability reform and addressing the rising cost of pharmaceuticals) that have to be made without worrying about political contributions or retributions from lobbyists and interest groups, this quagmire will continue, and our cost of care delivery will continue to rise in an exponential proportion. With increasing costs, more regulations will follow. While some of the regulations are beneficial, the majority of them have the unintended consequences of increasing the costs they are trying to contain.

Hospitals and physicians will continue to spend an exorbitant amount hiring regulatory and compliance specialists to help navigate the barrage of regulations. The physicians will remain the executors of the processes implemented by the hospitals to meet the compliance requirements while trying to provide excellent quality care. These physicians or care providers will continue to suffer silently in an attempt to meet the barrage of regulations. Eventually, the physicians will be burned out, depressed, dissuaded from practicing the profession they love, transition to a different pay (cash-based) model of medicine they can control, or exit the field entirely. If the physician is burned out, depressed, and unwell, how can the physician provide quality care that the government and the population deserve?

The well-being of every physician and healthcare provider is tantamount to the survival of the house of medicine. The current state of our healthcare system is untenable. We should be re-imagining the future of healthcare, and the changes should start with the physicians. We, as physicians, should start holding ourselves accountable and demanding to do better. Overutilization of resources is a known issue in medicine, and physicians are notoriously responsible for it. We, as physicians, need to put patient care ahead of profit-making and not try to become uber-rich from the practice of medicine.

As part of the granular work to curtail costs, physician organizations have identified some practice patterns that need to change in order to start championing the practice of cost-conscious medicine. An initiative trying to jump-start this is the "choosing wisely" campaign that was embraced by every specialty. The initiative basically reviewed and identified several common diagnoses by specialty and identified areas of unnecessary testing or wastes relating to each of the diagnoses that physicians can control. The goal is to provide evidence-based guidance, demonstrating that the current state of practice leads to overutilization with a consequential increase in the cost of care. Although this campaign is meant to start the conversation by highlighting areas that physicians can control, changes to practice patterns are very difficult, and it will take a lot of grassroots efforts to make sure the campaign is successful.

Since we live in the house of medicine, we need to work with hospital partners to collectively reduce the cost of care and do what we believe is right for our patients. Simultaneously, hospital partners need to be investing in the aspect that focuses on the "Whole Physician" or "Whole Provider"—how to make physicians or providers "whole." This can be accomplished by providing the resources needed to fully fund and operate centers for physician well-being. You cannot have a physician that is about to burn out or already burnt out, uncentered, morally injured, and unwell perform Whole-Patient or Patient-Centered Care. A healthy and whole physician with collaboration with the hospitals is needed to start the granular work to salvage the house of medicine within the constraints of what we can control.

However, the heavy legislative work relating to the other players (pharmaceutical companies, medical liability reform, insurance companies) will require a lot of intestinal fortitude from the legislators. Unfortunately, any iota of hope in the legislative process to address these other players is tantamount to living in the proverbial fantasy land. The so-called legislators are more preoccupied with their reelections and pandering to the influential donors from the players than legislating courageously. Here lies the major problem for the house of medicine.

(Footnotes)
[12] "Historical NHE, 2019."

[13] George J Schieber, "Health Expenditures in Major Industrialized Countries, 1960-87."

[14] Gerard F. Anderson and Jean-Pierre Poullier, "Health Spending, Access, and Outcomes."

[15] David U. Himmelstein et al., "A Comparison of Hospital Administrative Costs."

[16] W. Wynn-Jones et al., "Variation in Expenditure for Common."

[17] Jayne O'Donnell, "Huge Health Care Price Differences Even within Same Area, by State."

Chapter Four

Whole-Patient and Self Care

Are we practicing what we preach?

The concept of whole-patient care or patient-centered care initially was part of holistic medicine but is now considered mainstream medicine. Unfortunately, the promise of whole-patient care is too often negated by the dysfunctional environment in which care is delivered. The concept is predicated on the assumption or expectation that the healthcare provider not only addresses the patient's ailments but also addresses all aspects of health, from physical to emotional and psychological. It is postulated that if all these dimensions were addressed, some of the non-medical contributors to health-related issues or frequent hospital visits could be identified and as a result, appropriate referral or interventions could be coordinated as deemed necessary.

The whole-patient care concept is meant to address the physical, emotional, mental, social, and spiritual well-being of patients. Physical well-being addresses lifestyle behaviors that cultivate good health and help avoid preventable diseases. Emotional well-being addresses factors that affect the patient's state of mind like coping mechanisms and mental health conditions such as anxiety or depressive disorders. Spiritual well-being encompasses a universal human experience that addresses our purpose in life and can involve a religious affiliation or a deep sense of being interconnected with nature or the environment. And social well-being addresses the interactions and relationships with friends, family, and the community.

But who is to deliver this care? Obviously not healthcare executives or the institutions they serve. Physicians are tasked with delivering this care to the patients the healthcare organizations serve. The burning question is this: Can a disengaged, burnt-out, morally injured physician deliver whole-patient care?

This sounds like an oxymoron in itself. The irony here is that the philosophy is backward in its approach. For a physician to provide whole-patient or patient-centered care, the physician must be whole. In the era where almost fifty-five percent of physicians express some level of burnout, seventeen percent or so exhibit colloquial depression, and a physician commits suicide every day;[18, 19, 20] shouldn't healthcare organizations be investing first in physician wholeness?

It seems obvious Investing in the concept of physician wholeness should have been the first phase of the foundation of the patient-wholeness campaign. Can you imagine a physician that is not physically fit or healthy, emotionally drained and detached, spiritually wanting or lacking, and socially isolated or uninvolved trying to address the pillars of wholeness with a patient? The oddity and irony here are very obvious. Ironically, instead of focusing on physician wholeness and addressing burnout, we are engaged in programs to address physician resilience. This is a sure way to miss the mark.

Most physicians are resilient by virtue of being a physician. It takes a resilient person to make it through cut-throat medical school and survive the grueling and sometimes almost torture-like residency before transitioning to a full-fledged physician. This requires superb intestinal fortitude, the ability to tighten sphincter muscles, and possess the unique quality of equanimity under duress. The idea that physicians are not resilient and need resiliency training is insulting to practicing physicians.

The whole-patient or patient-centered care concept is a welcome addition to modern healthcare; it has been long overdue. Healthcare organizations serious about delivering whole-patient care need to deliberately and simultaneously invest in physician wellness. At the end of the day, it is only a whole physician that can effectively buy-in and deliver whole-patient care.

How does a physician or healthcare provider become whole? In order to understand this, we have to understand the definition of wholeness.

What is Wholeness?

According to the Oxford Dictionary, wholeness is defined as "the quality of being whole or complete." Simplistically speaking, a person that is broken and damaged, cannot be whole. Wholeness is a state of feeling fulfilled, satisfied, accomplished, healthy, and successful. The concept of wholeness closely mirrors the science of well-being. In order to understand wholeness and fully grasp the concept, for the purpose of this book, it will be discussed in the context of well-being.

What is Well-Being?

According to the Merriam-Webster Dictionary, well-being is defined as "the state of being happy, healthy, or prosperous." The science of well-being strives to uncover and promote the factors that enable individuals and communities to prosper and become whole. It classifies well-being into the following types: physical, spiritual, emotional, and social. These four components do not exist solely but are interconnected. For a person to be whole, the components of well-being must be in a state of harmony.

Achieving a state of well-being cannot occur without a clear strategy. Depending on individual situations, you can get a critical appraisal of your overall well-being using tools such as the Meaning in Life Questionnaire (MLQ), Flourishing scale, Grit Scale, Brief resilience scale, Satisfaction in Life scale, and the Gratitude Questionnaire. By using either or a combination of these scales, you can appraise your well-being status. Based on your appraisal, although the pillars of well-being are intertwined, you can determine which pillar requires immediate rectification. Approaching it this way, you can tackle one aspect of well-being at a time with a laser focus and gradually elevate your well-being status until you become whole. The overarching goal is to achieve a state of well-being, otherwise known as a state of being whole.

Case Study:
Dr. Justin Time is a busy solo internist who has always been active, exercises three days a week,

eats nutritious meals, is actively involved in his community, and has solid relationships with his wife and children. Over the past three years, he has become withdrawn due to the demands of his job. He stays late at work completing his charts, navigating the claims and denials from insurance companies, transitioning to electronic medical records, and managing the increasing demands of his patients. He barely has time to work out or engage in any physical activities; he thrives on fast foods and sometimes hardly eats. He is now overweight, withdrawn from social engagements, and his relationship with his wife is beginning to suffer. He often gets home late and is too tired to be involved in any meaningful conversation or activities, unable to sleep well at night because his mind is ruminating over incomplete tasks from the prior day. He is fully engrossed with his job, trying to navigate the unending changes and regulations in healthcare today. Do you know anyone like Dr. Justin Time? Sound familiar?

Well, I was once like Dr. Justin Time. The implementation of the electronic health records and the chartings and the documentation involved was a culture shock. I began to feel like I was overpaid performing clerical duties. It was difficult to complete my charts during my allotted shift times. Often, I stayed behind after my shift for two to three hours completing my charts or sometimes, due to sheer exhaustion from the rigors of the shift, I could not wait to exit the emergency department. Consequently, I ended up attempting to complete my charts at home. In essence, I spent all my days working. I hardly socialized or even exercised due to exhaustion and was too fatigued to engage my

wife and children in any meaningful activities or conversations.

As if EHR (electronic health records) was not painful enough, here comes the implementation of the lean process in the emergency department. The lean process originates from the manufacturing industry, specifically Toyota. This manufacturing principle is often referred to as "Just in time." Basically, it is a form of efficiency management that strives to eliminate waste along any structured process. In the emergency department, the lean process requires patients that are deemed stable to be moved to a so-called holding or observation area filled with reclining chairs in order to create room for patients waiting in the lobby to be seen in a timely manner. I constantly have to explain this rationale to the patients that are dumbfounded by the idea.

When patients visit the emergency department, the majority of them are scared and anxious. When they are finally settled into a room, and their anxiety is slowly abating, all of a sudden, we have to displace them into a bank of strangers in a holding area. This, to me, was unconscionable and violated the ordinance of common respect for others. I constantly struggle with this, and this struggle came to a boiling point when a woman who had just completed a miscarriage, traumatized and shocked, was whisked to the holding area while waiting to be picked up by her husband. She was grieving and needed a quiet place, which in this situation was the comfort of an ED room. The question I wrangled with at the time was, "How do I keep patients safe and protected in their lowest hour if I keep moving them from place to place?"

This was a very tough one for me to handle. At this point, I felt like my role as a physician had been subjugated to that of a marginalized assembly line worker that had lost every moral compass of decency for which the lean concept was initially designed. I arrived at a crossroads and started questioning if this was the medical career I signed up for. I felt dissuaded, becoming more disengaged with the whole process; I felt morally injured and began to contemplate if I could ever continue to practice medicine in this environment.

Back to Dr. Justin Time. As you can see, he is in over his head. He is heading towards burnout, or what is now referred to as "moral injury," which is what many physicians are wrangling with at this moment. His well-being is in a state of chaos, and he is not whole, as his physical, emotional, and social well-being are in disarray. Without intervention, we can all imagine the punch line of his story. Should his story or your story end this way? I hope not. We all have the power to change our story. I changed my story, and I hope to help you change yours.

How can you change your story? How did I change my story? As I embarked on my journey, I asked myself the question, "How do I become whole?" As I pondered this question, I had to research the concept of being whole. The research into this took me into an entirely new dimension. I understood that for my survival and sanity, it was imperative I perform due diligence and be willing to reconfigure the way I currently operate. I thoroughly studied the concept of whole-patient care and the component of wholeness that I was tasked to apply to all my patient encounters. As I looked

in the mirror, it dawned on me that all these components of wholeness (physical, emotional, spiritual, and social) should be applied to me first before I could have the audacity to discuss them with my patients. My research led me to the understanding that these four components of wholeness lack an entity that's integral to the well-being of physicians. That component is mental well-being or wholeness. As it has been documented in several papers, a lot of healthcare workers are suffering in silence from mental health issues. Consequently, I coined what I referred to as my five pillars, or dimensions, of wholeness (physical, emotional, mental, spiritual, and social).

The Five Pillars of Well-Being and Wholeness

As I began my journey toward becoming whole, I had to perform a self-wellness inventory with a reflective introspection. While formulating the foundational works, my research led me to what I refer to as the "Five Pillars of Wholeness." These pillars are physical well-being, emotional well-being, mental well-being, spiritual well-being, and social well-being. I needed a specific objective with goals that are achievable if placed in the proper context. While there are several dimensions of wholeness, the ones I believe will allow me to be laser-focused are my five pillars. The following chapters will explore these five pillars of well-being.

(Footnotes)

[18] Matteo Nunner, "Medscape National Physician Burnout & Depression Report 2018."

[19] Lisa S. Rotenstein et al., "Prevalence of Burnout among Physician."

[20] Thomas P Reith, "Burnout in United States Healthcare Professionals."

Chapter Five

The First Pillar: Physical Well-Being

Physical well-being means being physically well in all dimensions of health. It is the aspect of life that involves caring for the health of the body to keep it in top function and in an emotionally balanced state. People who physically-well tend to experience better mental and emotional well-being. Simply speaking, it measures the overall health status. A more concise definition describes physical well-being as the ability to perform physical activities and carry out social roles that are not hindered by physical limitations and experiences of bodily pain and biological health indicators.[21]

The physical self-motivates and determines behaviors and contributes to mental health and overall well-being.[22] The direct correlation between physical wellness and mental and emotional wellness and vice versa is an example of the interconnectedness of the pillars of wellness. The psychological phenomenon of optimism in the pillar of emotional wellness has been shown to promote both mental and physical wellness by fostering a higher quality of life and healthy lifestyles.[23]

The daily dynamics of life, if not monitored, could have significant negative effects on physical health. Occupational stress and type A behavior have been shown to have a significant impact on physical well-being.[4] This supports the theory that emotional states due to overwhelming stress have a deleterious effect on physical well-being by virtue of lifestyle choices that are often embarked upon during these situations.

To improve physical well-being, habits that promote physical activities/exercise, proper sleep patterns, adequate stress management, and healthy dietary choices must be cultivated. There are many elements of physical well-being, such as physical activities, stress management, sleep adequacy, body image, nutrition, addiction, safety, hygiene, relaxation, and much more. For the purpose of this discussion, emphasis will be placed on the following: physical activities, sleep patterns, stress management, healthy dietary choices, and relaxation. It is important to understand that the utmost goal of this pillar is to optimize the management of current health statuses of those with underlying medical conditions and to prevent the development of health issues by cultivating habits that minimize the development of diseases.

Physical Activity: Your Most Important Thirty Minutes

These are activities that keep you in top physical shape and in good health. According to the World Health Organization (WHO), physical activity is defined as any bodily movement produced by skeletal muscles that require energy expenditure.[25] It is important not to misconstrue physical activity with exercise because by definition, they are two different entities. Physical activities are everyday activities such as household chores, yard work, activities undertaken while working, or engaging in any sort of recreational activities. Exercises, on the other hand, are structured activities used to achieve a certain level of physical fitness goals. Exercise is a subcategory of physical activity. In essence, physical activities keep your heart pumping, build your cardiovascular endurance, improve muscle strength, maintain strong bones, control body weight, and increase cognition and mental agility.

According to WHO, one in four adults globally is not active enough. Insufficient physical activity is one of the leading risk factors for death worldwide as well as non-communicable diseases such as cardiovascular, cancer, and diabetes. To maximize the effects of physical activities, WHO recommended that adults aged 18 to 64 should do a minimum of 150 minutes of moderately intense physical activity throughout the week, or at least 75 minutes of vigorous-intensity throughout the week, or an equivalent combination of both.[26] For full health benefits, it is imperative that physical activity should be of moderate and vigorous-intensity. To fully maximize the benefits of exercise, performing more than the required minimum would be my recommendation. The table below lists some examples of these activities, frequencies, intensities, and durations.

Groups	Activities	Frequency	Intensity	Duration
Children and Youth	Aerobics	Daily	Moderate + Vigorous	60 minutes (minimum 3x/week)
Adults (18-64 years)+	Aerobics	Weekly	Moderate	150 minutes (minimum)
Older Adults	Aerobics	Weekly	Vigorous + Muscle Training	75 minutes (minimum)

Table 1: Adapted from Activities recommendations by WHO and CDC

In 1995, the most widely known evidence-based physical activity recommendation for public health was issued by the U.S. Centers for Disease Control and Prevention (CDC) and the American College of Sports Medicine (ACSM). It reads: "Every U.S. adult should accumulate 30 minutes or more of moderate-intensity physical activities on most, preferably all days of the week."[27] While this recommendation was widely accepted worldwide, the American Heart Association (AHA), in conjunction with the ACSM in 2007, published the findings of their extensive evidence-based review of the benefits of physical activities and recommended that: "All healthy adults need a moderate-intensity aerobic activity for a minimum of 30 minutes on five days a week or vigorous-intensity aerobic activity for a minimum of 20 minutes on three days each week to promote and maintain health."[28]

The benefits of regular physical activities are innumerable. They reduce the risk of noncommunicable diseases (hypertension, coronary heart disease, stroke, diabetes, and various types of cancer), improve muscle tones, bones, and functional health, cardiorespiratory fitness, control body weight, increase mental agility, and prevent falls and vertebrae fractures. One study provided further insight into the role physical inactivity plays in the development of chronic diseases and premature death; the study confirmed there is irrefutable evidence of the effectiveness of regular physical activity in the primary and secondary prevention of several chronic diseases (cardiovascular diseases, diabetes, cancer, hypertension, obesity, depression, and osteoporosis) and premature death. The study also noted a linear relationship between physical activity and health status, such that a further increase in physical activity and fitness will lead to an additional improvement in overall health.[29]

Those of us who are high achievers with demanding job obligations must devise strategies that incorporate structured physical activity into our daily routine to reap all its benefits. It's unacceptable to say we are too busy to make time for this. This is necessary for our sanity, mental agility, and intestinal fortitude to withstand the duress of our daily grind. Understanding that physical activity does not have to be structured, we can utilize innovative ways while at work to meet some of these needs. A typical example is to challenge yourself to take 10,000 brisk steps daily or use the stairs instead of the elevator or the escalator. These two alone could count for moderate-intensity activities. However, it is also important to find time for mental release after work to squeeze in more activities, even if only for fifteen to thirty minutes. Activities such as running, racquetball, cycling, high-intensity interval training, swimming, or any aerobic exercises will suffice.

My favorite physical activity is running. Running frees my mind and spirit and it allows me to reconnect with nature and my surroundings. Running might not be for everyone, but for those that choose this activity, the health benefits make it worth all the effort. There is evidence that supports the health benefits of running. A study published in the *British Journal of Sports Medicine* that investigated the association of running participation and dose of running with the risk of all-cause cardiovascular and cancer mortality. The results showed that running participation is associated with a twenty-seven percent lower risk of all-cause and mortality, a thirty percent decrease in cardiovascular mortality, and a twenty-three percent decrease in cancer mortality. This was a meta-analysis of fourteen studies from six prospective cohorts with a sample of 232,149 pooled participants. The overall conclusion is that increased participation in running probably led to substantial improvement in population health and longevity and any amount of running is better than none.[30]

With demanding schedules in a world that is not slowing down anytime soon, participating in physical activities may not need to be structured to get some benefits; however, it is imperative that you have a structured regimen that your schedule will adequately accommodate to harness the full mental, psychological, spiritual, and overall well-being benefits. Having a structured regimen means you are committed and are making it an integral part of your daily agenda. At the end of the day, the goal is to engage in whichever activities allow you to accomplish the intensity recommended by WHO to reward yourself with the full health benefits.

Sleep: Our Biggest Problem

Are you getting adequate sleep? Lack of adequate sleep used to be my nemesis until I changed my routine. As we all know, a third of our lives are spent sleeping. It is an integral part of our daily routine. One of the necessities for survival and increased mental alertness is quality sleep. Without adequate sleep, pathways in the brain that generate new memories, mental agility, and alertness are compromised.

Although the biological purpose of sleep remains mysterious, the functioning of every facet of the body (brain, heart, lungs, metabolism, immune response, emotion, mood, and response to disease) is affected by the quality and quantity of sleep. Several diseases such as hypertension, cardiovascular disease, diabetes, obesity, and depression are inadvertently linked to chronic lack of or poor-quality sleep.

Additionally, lack of sleep impacts relationships and can have both financial and economic repercussions. At the 2013 Society of Personality and Social Psychology (SPSP) annual meeting, research presented by scientists from UC Berkeley claimed that inadequate sleep could impair our ability to appreciate our partners and loved ones, which can lead to stress and tension in relationships. Their report also showed that inadequate sleep means fewer feelings of gratitude and higher levels of selfishness.

Regarding economic and financial repercussions, poor sleep has a costly impact and often tragic consequences on society. According to the U.S. Department of Health and Human Services, chronic sleepiness costs the nation $16 billion in healthcare expenditure every year and an estimated $50 billion in lost productivity annually. The department further stated that insomniacs lose about 11.3 days of productivity every year, costing companies about $2,280 per person. According to the National Highway Traffic Safety Administration, drowsy driving causes 100,000 car crashes each year, costing about $12.5 million annually.

To further understand the value of sleep, it is important to be familiar with the biological process of sleep. Several structures within the brain itself are involved in sleep. The **hypothalamus** contains groups of nerve cells that control centers that affect sleep and arousal; the **suprachiasmatic nucleus (SCN)** within the hypothalamus receives light exposure information directly from the eyes and controls behavioral rhythm; **the brain stem** communicates with the hypothalamus to control transitions between wake and sleep cycles. Sleep-promoting cells within the hypothalamus and the brain stem produce the chemical GABA, which reduces activity in the arousal centers. The **thalamus** acts as a relay for information from the senses to the cerebral cortex; it becomes quiet during most stages of sleep and allows the brain to tune out the external world; however, it is active during rapid-eye-movement (REM) sleep, and it constantly sends images, sounds, and other sensations to the cerebral cortex to constitute dreams.[31]

The **pineal gland** receives signals from the SCN to produce the hormone melatonin. This hormone allows us to fall asleep when lights are out. The peaks and valleys of melatonin are believed by scientists to be responsible for matching the body's circadian rhythm to external cycles of light and darkness. **The basal forebrain** supposedly promotes the stages of sleep and wakefulness, while parts of the mid-brain act as the arousal system. The chemical compound adenosine released from the basal forebrain and other regions supposedly supports sleep drive, something caffeine counteracts because it's a stimulant, which is why it keeps people awake. Lastly, the amygdala facilitates the processing of emotions and becomes very active during REM sleep.[32]

It is important to have a quick window into the two internal biological mechanisms (circadian rhythms and sleep-wake homeostasis) that work together to regulate sleep-wake cycles. The circadian rhythms, according to the National Institute of General Medical Sciences, are physical, mental, and behavioral changes that follow a daily cycle. They respond mostly to light and darkness in the environment. In addition to influencing the sleep-wake cycle, they affect hormone release, eating habits, digestion, body temperature, and other important bodily functions. The body's biological clock, which is based on a 24-hour cycle, controls the circadian rhythms. The effects of the biological clock on the circadian rhythms are controlled by the body's master clock, which is composed of thousands of neurons called the Suprachiasmatic nucleus (SCN) that was described earlier.[33]

Sleep-wake homeostasis, on the other hand, is believed to be the main regulatory process in sleep. It has a strong influence on the depth and maintenance of sleep.[34] The sleep homeostatic process is basically a rise in sleep pressure during periods of wakefulness with subsequent dissipation during sleep. Homeostasis in this context refers to the compensatory facilitation of deep, continuous, and long sleep episodes when sleep is initiated after a prolonged period of wakefulness.[35] A Preponderance of evidence has confirmed that sleep homeostasis and the circadian process regulate the quantity, quality, and timing of sleep and wakefulness.[36]

Now that we have a brief understanding of the biological process of sleep and the two major internal regulators of sleep, it is our prerogative to minimize activities that might jeopardize the harmonious process of sleep. The saying that sleep is the time for the brain to shut down and rest is a total myth. Scientists now understand that neither the body nor the brain shut down during sleep but rather work harder than periods of wakefulness. The brain undergoes a process of cell restoration, processing information, and improving health. In essence, the lack of adequate sleep prevents these restorative processes from taking place.

It's now best to ask: why is sleep important to overall well-being? Well, as earlier stated, one of the utmost important necessities for survival and increased mental alertness is quality sleep. Without adequate sleep, pathways in the brain that generate new memories, mental agility, and alertness are compromised. Additionally, lack of adequate sleep has a deleterious effect on body homeostasis, mental agility, alertness, performances, and overall emotional states. Simply stated, lack of adequate sleep disrupts the body's homeostasis, leading to several diseases such as hypertension, cardiovascular disease, diabetes, obesity, and depression.

One of the important components of physical well-being is diet and nutrition to maintain a healthy weight. Lack of sleep has been linked to the obesity epidemic in the United States. According to the National Sleep Foundation, between 1960 and 2002, the proportion of young adults getting fewer than seven hours of sleep per night more than doubled.[37] This decreases sleep duration and has a linear relationship with the obesity epidemic. As we discuss this relationship, it is important to mention two regulatory hormones (Leptin and Ghrelin) that inform the brain about the status of energy balance.[38] These hormones are peripheral signals that contribute to the central regulation of food intake. Studies have shown that the circulating leptin levels rapidly decrease or increase in response to acute caloric shortages or surpluses. Changes in leptin have been associated with the reciprocal change in hunger status.[39] Ghrelin peptides, on the other hand, are produced in the stomach and their contribution to energy balance is to stimulate the appetite.

A study by Guglielmo Beccuti et al., evaluating the relationship between sleep and obesity in their meta-analysis demonstrated that the obesity epidemic had been paralleled by a trend in reduced sleep duration. They also surmised that sleep is an important modulator of neuroendocrine function and glucose metabolism. Sleep loss causes metabolic and endocrine alterations that lead to decreased glucose tolerance, decreased insulin sensitivity, increased levels of ghrelin, decreased levels of leptin, and increased hunger and appetite.[40]

Spiegel K, et al. conducted a study to determine whether partial sleep curtailment, an increasingly prevalent behavior, alters appetite regulations. The study measured plasma leptin and ghrelin levels and subjective rating of hunger and appetite after periods of partial sleep curtailment. The results of the study showed a decrease in anorexigenic hormones like leptin and an increase in orexigenic factors, like ghrelin, as well as an increase in hunger and appetite, especially for calorie-dense foods with high carbohydrates.[41] The science of sleep and obesity has provided us a preponderance of evidence[42, 43, 44] that sleep is a significant contributor to obesity by virtue of its impact on the two important energy-regulatory peptides that respond to energy homeostasis.

What about the impact of sleep deprivation on the cardiovascular system? The homeostasis imbalance of lack of adequate sleep percolates into the body's entire physiologic make-up. As scientists understand more about the impacts of sleep deprivation, more studies are being published to highlight its effects on the cardiovascular system. A study published in the *Journal of Psychosomatic Medicine* looking at cardiovascular reactivity to acute psychosocial stress following sleep deprivation demonstrated significant interactions between sleep deprivation and stress on systolic blood pressure. They noted that systolic blood pressure was higher in sleep-deprived samples compared to those with normal sleep. Based on the findings, the authors postulated that sleep loss might increase cardiovascular risks by the dysregulation of stress physiology.[45]

Another systematic and meta-analytical review study looking at the potential epidemiological evidence for the link between sleep duration and high blood pressure was published in the *Journal of Sleep Medicine.* The study included a total of 225,858 subjects in the analysis, and they demonstrated a U-shaped relationship between habitual sleep duration and hypertension at the cross-sectional level. They concluded that short sleep duration was associated with a higher risk of hypertension even longitudinally.[46]

Effects of sleep debt on overall cardiovascular health have been established by a preponderance of the evidence. As we begin to understand more about these effects, it is imperative to consider sleep as a modifiable risk factor affecting overall cardiovascular health. As we try to modify this risk factor, it is also important to make the public aware of these facts: If you sleep well, you can decrease your risks of cardiovascular diseases.

Just as sleep deprivation affects homeostasis and every facet of physiologic functioning, its effect on the psychological and emotional states cannot be overstated. If you look at yourself in the mirror on days you have accumulated sleep debt, what do you see? Do you see a happy-go-lucky person or a disgruntled, mentally fatigued, exasperated person?

Well, lack of sleep tends to bring out the parts of us we do not really like to see.

What is sleep debt? When a person gets a less-than-adequate amount of sleep, this is referred to as sleep deprivation. However, whenever an individual has multiple days of sleep deprivation, they enter a state of "sleep debt," which is a cumulative effect of insufficient sleep for any period of time.[47, 48]

Several studies in addition to the above have shown the impact of sleep deprivation on mood and emotional states. A recently published systematic review shows that a large body of research supports the connection between sleep deprivation and mood changes such as increased anger and aggression. Additionally, they showed that individuals who get adequate amounts of sleep each night exhibit fewer emotional outbursts, such as anger, and display fewer aggressive behaviors.[49]

Case Study:

This is my story. After several verbal assaults at work trying to appease sometimes irrational demands from my patients, I go home exhausted and extremely drained while ruminating on why I allow myself to be subjected to the constant assault on my intellectual capacity by the patients I am trying to help. I make a quick bowl of cereal, grab the remote, and turn the television on to catch up on the daily news while balancing my laptop on my outstretched legs. Despite knowing that what was emanating from the television was noise to me, it was an escape from my reality. This was an extremely sad and low point for me. The next thing I know, it is almost midnight. When I decide to turn the television off and retire to my bed, I just lie there waiting for sleep to come. By the time I finally fall asleep, it is time to wake up. I am exhausted, mentally fatigued, emotionally labile, and cognitively inept from lack of sleep as I embark on my commute to work. The drives to work are often fraught with anger, agitation, and outbursts at any traffic occurrences such as cars traveling too slow, not making the right turn at a stop sign on time, or someone simply making the mistake of cutting in front of my car (does this remind you of anyone you know?). I eventually found out this was unhealthy, and I needed a drastic change before I suffered a stroke from my wanton outbursts caused by my sleep deprivation and accumulated sleep debt.

As I embarked on my journey to wholeness, I realized it was imperative to control my own story. It is my story, and I am empowered to rewrite it. So how did I rewrite my story? Well, I started by performing a personal life inventory with deliberate introspection into who I was, who I had become, and where I was going. I identified sleep deprivation and sleep debt as an integral component of where I was at the time. Additionally, I identified other factors such as changes in the healthcare infrastructure and environment, the demands on providers, and the fact that I am morally injured. I quickly understood that to tackle all these epic tsunamis; I needed to start with the one I could easily control.

I identified sleep as my first step. If I needed to get myself right, it had to start with the right emotional mindset and cognitive assertiveness. Having adequate sleep would be the foundation of my transformation. I decided to change my routine, and I became determined to have between seven to eight hours of sleep a night. How did I accomplish this? The first thing I did when I got home was to take a quick shower, grab a bite, and stay the hell away from the remote. After my evening meal, I spent quality time with my family before I even contemplated touching the remote. If I did touch the remote to catch up on daily news, my television time did not exceed forty-five minutes. After forty-five minutes, the television was turned off, and I grabbed a book, sat on my recliner, and read while watching the sunset. Consistently, I am now in bed between 8:00 p.m. and 8:30 p.m. on weekdays. This requires discipline and consistency. I routinely wake up at 4:30 a.m. after eight hours of good sleep; I head to the gym, get a quick thirty-minute workout, take a long shower, and am out of the house energized with the right mind frame at 5:30 a.m. for my 6:00 a.m. shift. Driving to work is peaceful and uneventful with my gospel or inspirational music, and long gone is the anger and aggression that led to the traffic outbursts.

Since taking control of my story, I feel healthier and alive just because of a healthy night of sleep. I used to be one of those that insisted it's impossible to get seven to eight hours of sleep with our schedule. This was because I let my story control me. Once I took control of my story, no excuses accepted, I stayed focused and disciplined. What is a good night's sleep worth to you? Now that we understand that one of the most important necessities for survival and mental alertness is the quality of sleep, it should definitely be worth a lot to you, and can be the motivation that is needed to change your story. So, take control of your sleep and re-write your story!

Stress: The Enemy We Hide

Work-related stress is at an all-time high, and employees and employers are feeling the brunt of it. The constant struggles with demanding workloads, inadequate supplies to accomplish tasks efficiently, staff shortages, perceived unsupportive managers, incessant efforts to cut costs, and the blurred line between work and personal life contribute to driving up the level of stress in the workplace. Overwhelming stress impacts performances, engagements, health, and quality of life. At present, almost nine in ten adults believe that stress can contribute to the development of illnesses such as coronary heart disease, depression, obesity. and that some types of stress can trigger heart attacks or arrhythmias. Additionally, many working Americans continue to report symptoms of stress, with forty-two percent reporting irritability or anger; thirty-seven percent fatigue; thirty-five percent a lack of interest, motivation, and energy; thirty-two percent headaches; and twenty-four percent upset stomachs due to stress.[50]

Case Study:

Meet Dr. Q. He is a well-regarded internist with a thriving practice. He is one of those rare internists that still admits and takes care of his patients in the hospital. The toll of the changing dynamics in healthcare (electronic health records, bundled payments, decreasing reimbursements, and the need to see more patients compensate for the decreased insurance reimbursements) is becoming apparent. The time to discharge his patients is much later in the day, and the length of stay of his admitted patients is at the lower end of the percentile rank. He has also seen an uptick in the code of conducts filed against him by the nurses caring for his patients and some of his colleagues. Recently, Dr. Q was observed chastising a nurse in front of a patient and storming out of the room in a profanity-laced tirade that attracted the attention of the hospital administration and the medical staff leadership.

Owing to the concerns for the well-being of this well-respected physician, Dr. Q was mandated to visit the department of professionalism and physician support services. Does Dr. Q seem familiar to you? Or do you believe you are slowly gravitating toward Dr. Q's behavior? Can you relate to the dilemma this clinician is dealing with?

In the current healthcare state, healthcare providers are feeling the impact of all the changing dynamics. When you compound these with the incessant demand for quality care in the context of increased patient volume contact within a narrow period, quality metrics, increased patient experience, and satisfaction scores that are ultimately linked to overall compensations, it's easy to understand why stress levels in the healthcare environment are at an all-time high. Similar to the healthcare environment, leaders and managers in every industry are dealing with the same quandary to meet the margins and improve productivity and efficiencies with the resulting overwhelming stress burden.

As healthcare providers, adaptation and resilience are our fortitudes. We adapt easily to changes and are always willing to do what is right for patient care. However, too frequent changes create frustration, angst, and resentment, which will inadvertently affect productivity, create a chaotic work environment, non-engaging medical staff, decreased quality of provided care and patient experience, and, of course, burnout and moral injury.

In an attempt to comprehend the importance of stress responses, it is imperative to understand the neurobiology of stress. First, the adrenal glands produce stress hormones. There are several stress hormones produced by this organ, but the main ones are cortisol, adrenaline, norepinephrine, DHEA, and dopamine. Each of these hormones is responsible for mediating specific receptors based on the type of stress to be modulated. These hormones exert protective effects on the overall homeostasis and are released as needed to meet daily challenges. However, in the presence of persistent stress, these hormones may exert their deleterious effects on the body.

The main stress-response hormone is cortisol. This hormone is produced in the adrenal cortex and is stimulated by the adrenocorticotropic hormone (ACTH), which receives its signal from a corticotropin-releasing hormone (CRH), which is produced by the hypothalamic-pituitary axis.[51] Cortisol has the following effect on the body: increased blood sugar for glycogen storage; enhanced gluconeogenesis from protein, fat, and carbohydrates; produces insulin resistance; maintains normal blood pressure; feedback regulates the hypothalamic-pituitary axis; regulates adrenaline production; and suppresses the immune system. As you can see, the impact of elevated cortisol levels on body homeostasis is significant. Knowing that cortisol is released in response to stress, living in a world with insurmountable stress is an important contributor to the presence of preventable non-communicable diseases. Think about it for a second; persistently elevated cortisol is a risk factor for hypertension, diabetes, cardiovascular disease, obesity, delayed wound healing, osteoporosis, predisposition to infections, and sleep disturbance.

At any given time in the body, the fluctuation of cortisol follows the ultradian rhythm cycle. Unlike a circadian rhythm, which is a cycle that is completed once daily, the ultradian cycle is recurrent periods or cycles repeated throughout the day. This fluctuation or variation is in essence mediated by exposure to stressful stimuli or situations.[52, 53] Cortisol, in addition to stress responses, also modulates cognition. It has been shown that cortisol has an inverted U-shaped relationship with cognition, and very low or high levels impair cognition, while moderate elevation tends to facilitate the acquisition and retention of memories.[54] In essence, a low or higher-than-normal level of cortisol has a deleterious effect on mental action and the process of acquiring knowledge and understanding through thought, experiences, and the senses. Knowing these facts, why would you want to let stress overrun you?

We all need some level of stress to stay alive. Without any stress, you might as well be dead. Life is filled with ups and downs. Embracing the ups and leaving enough behind to deal with the downs is the way to go. When you think of the way the heartbeats, you can see that life itself is up and down. When the heart beats, it's rhythmic as it goes up and down and cycles over and over. When this continues, you stay alive. But when the heartbeat flatlines, that means you are dead. Your life cannot just be flat; it needs the ups and downs to keep you going. However, how you manage the ups and downs is a different story.

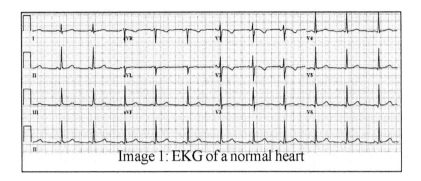

Image 1: EKG of a normal heart

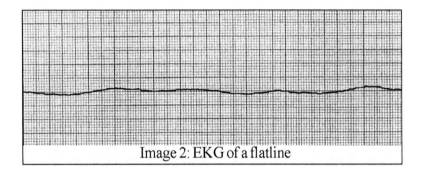

Image 2: EKG of a flatline

The other iteration of this is when the heart is in a state of dysrhythmia. You feel unwell, and depending on the rhythm, it may require immediate intervention. When you apply this to life, too many ups and downs or too much stress or inability to manage stress will ultimately lead to a state of distress.

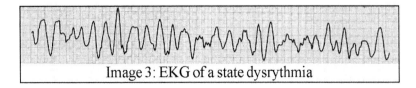

Image 3: EKG of a state dysrythmia

Several studies have shown the relationship between stress and performance. According to the Yorke-Dodson law, there is a relationship between arousal and behavioral performance, such that there is an optimal level of arousal for optimal performance. Over or under arousal reduces task performance.[55] In essence, we all need some level of arousal or stress for optimal performance. The stress curve below demonstrates this theory. How do you balance this, though?

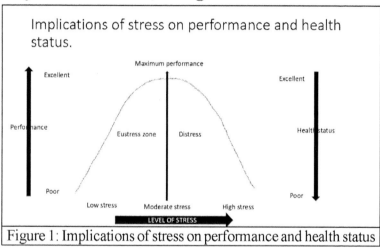

Figure 1: Implications of stress on performance and health status

According to the chart, which shows the relationship between performance and stress levels, as stress levels increase, there is a subsequent increase in performance until peak performance is attained. As stress levels continue to increase, performance begins to suffer. If this state of high stress persists, then fatigue, exhaustion, anxiety, impaired performance, and burnout manifests. Extremely low stress leads to boredom, while a very high level of stress leads to anxiety, distress, and burnout if allowed to persist for an extended duration. The implications of this on the overall health status cannot be overstated. As the figure demonstrates, as the stress level increases, the overall health status continues to deteriorate simultaneously.

Optimal performance is achieved within the so-called "Eustress" or "functional stress zone." The majority of high performers are most productive at this sweet spot. What is unique about this zone is that when the task is completed, the stress response hormones return to basal levels, thus avoiding the deleterious effect of persistent stress. Below is another simplified iteration of the performance-stress curve.

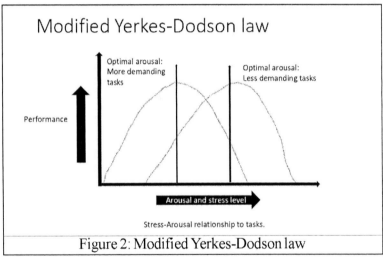

Figure 2: Modified Yerkes-Dodson law

Taking a look at figure 2 above, which demonstrates another iteration of the Yerkes-Dodson law, it is interesting to see that different complexities of tasks could be accomplished at different stress or arousal levels. The more demanding tasks could be accomplished within the eustress zone. However, at the peak level of stress, less demanding tasks could be easily completed.

To achieve optimal balance without migrating towards stress overdrive, it is important that less demanding, easily completable tasks should ideally be undertaken when the perceived stress level is elevated.

Stress management is an integral component of well-being. I subscribe to the notion that we stress a lot over things we cannot control. I ask you to practice this simple exercise of writing down the top ten things that bring you the most stress. Take a good look at these stressors. Now, cross out the ones you believe are out of your control or you cannot do anything about. How many do you have left? Now take an introspective look at your list and ask yourself this question: "Why am I stressing over things I cannot control?" Why are you spending your mental energy ruminating over things that are beyond your control?

A better approach is to look at your list, identify the ones you think you can realistically address, and develop strategies to mitigate and potentially eradicate them, thus freeing your mental capacity to focus on more productive endeavors. Mind you; this will not be easy. Every decision has a price. I remember learning in economics a long time ago that the investor's opportunity cost the cost of the forgone alternatives. The question now is which alternatives are you willing to forgo and at what cost? Your biggest stressor may require life-altering changes. It may involve quitting your job, working less, making less, changing relationships with your spouse, family, or friends, or even relocation.

As you can see, stress is a big deal. The ability to function within the constraint of functional stress is the goal. Too little stress creates boredom and loss of motivation or intrinsic drive. On the other hand, too much stress leads to a state of distress, anxiety, angst, panic, and eventual breakdown and burnout, if not recognized and promptly addressed. Each individual has a sweet spot of stress needed to perform optimally. Know your sweet spot and devise mitigating your routine when you identify that you are about to cross over your sweet spot. If you can accomplish this, you are guaranteed to be in the "Eustress," or beneficial stress zone.

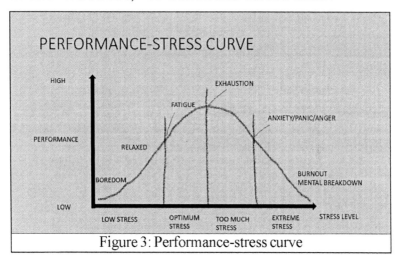

Figure 3: Performance-stress curve

Accomplishing the so-called "Eustress Zone" also requires a favorable quality of work-life. What is the quality of your work-life environment? Based on recent cutting-edge research by Professor Marko Kesti,[56] measuring the quality of work-life and assessing its impact on both employee engagement and productivity demonstrated that employees with low quality of work-life scores were at a much greater risk of burnout than those with higher scores.

The quality of work-life index calculation for healthcare providers may include the following questions scored on a scale of one to five: working environments, workload, and the ability to deliver preferred quality care, the balance of work and family, shift work, fair and equitable compensation, trust in organizational leadership, lack of involvement in decision making, professional isolation, loss of autonomy, lack of recognition, and poor relationship with peers or supervisors. As you can see, a low index score has significant implications for the life and productivity of the provider. In essence, healthcare organizations should work with healthcare providers to create a quality work-life environment to minimize the stress burden and create a "Eustress Zone."

So, how did Dr. Q, a well-respected physician with impeccable character, find himself in a situation where he had to be referred to the department of professionalism and physician support services to continue as a member of the medical staff? Well, Dr. Q was under enormous duress. The increased demands of the job due to incessant regulatory changes had overwhelmed him. He spent too much time charting on his electronic health record (EHR) template, as he was not technologically savvy, while his lobby became packed with patients waiting much longer to see him. Out of courtesy, he tried to see all his patients and closed his office around 5 p.m. Mind you; this was unusual for him. Ordinarily, his office hours were done by 2 p.m., after which he did his rounds for his patients in the hospital (he often had about fifteen active patients). During his office hours, he was getting inundated with calls to expedite the discharge of his patients in the hospital. These incessant calls frustrated him to the point that he started yelling at the callers and telling them he would discharge them when he was done with his office patients.

After Dr. Q made rounds on his patients later in the day for about three hours in the hospital, he headed back to his office to finish his charts before heading home around 9:30 p.m. He barely eats anything but junk food all day. By the time he gets home, his kids are in bed, and his wife is struggling to stay up for him. His relationship with his family is suffering simultaneously with his patient care. The overwhelming stress that led to burnout, or moral injury, that he is quietly dealing with is now manifesting as behavioral changes that are incongruent with his character. As part of the services provided by the physician support services, a strategy is devised to help this respected physician thrive and ease the stress burden he is carrying. He is convinced to use hospitalist services to care for his admitted patients (begrudgingly; he accepts a trial period, as he is concerned about revenue losses), and physician scribes' services or reliable dictation services are given to him to explore, though he realizes every recommendation increases his expenses. However, when informed that using a scribe service will allow him to see almost two to three more patients an hour and improve the efficiency, productivity, and patients' experiences in his office practice, he embraces it since its revenue-neutral.

Fast forward six months later, Dr. Q is loving his life. He does not see patients in the hospital anymore, and all his charts are completed in a timely manner. He has seen a significant increase in his patient volume that he was able to accommodate due to increased efficiency, and he is home by 5:30 p.m. daily and has no need to visit the hospital on weekends to see patients; his relationship with his family has improved significantly as a result. The health benefits of mitigating his stress include controlled hypertension and diabetes, weight-loss, improved diet, and better sleep. Additionally, the lost revenue for not admitting to the hospital was supplemented by increased office-patient volume and improved quality of life.

Which Dr. Q would you like to be? The one six months earlier or the new and improved one?

Dr. Q was fortunate to have access to resources or medical staff that enabled him to turn around his situation. The story that follows is that of Bobby, whose job-related stressors, and his approach to dealing with the stress landed him in the Emergency room.

Hi! I am Bobby, and this is my story. I am a fifty-six-year-old newly appointed executive director of a very successful company. My new role was accompanied by a lot of new demands: streamline the workforce, trim the margins, increase productivity and profitability. Although my background adequately prepared me to meet such demands, the pace of the demands was becoming untenable. I arrived at work early and often left much later at night. I barely saw my kids, as they were asleep when I came home from work and when I left for work. Time spent with my wife was marginalized. My weekends were filled with phone calls and wrapping up loose ends of the week. It never stopped. My sleep pattern was out of whack. I barely had a restful night's sleep as I spent all night ruminating about the day ahead. Do I sound like someone you know?

I started to drink more than normal at night to help me sleep. Over time, which wasn't working for me anymore. My primary care doctor prescribed me some sleeping pills and something to help me relax, but my stress level from the job was slowly killing me. The next thing I knew, I was introduced to cocaine. This is where my story gets real. Every time I snorted, it made me feel good, and all that stress or the overwhelming sense of defeat disappeared. I started getting used to feeling good and just rolling with whatever demands the job threw at me until one fateful day. On this day, it was before the mid-cycle performance review. I went to my car prior to my meeting, snorted some cocaine, and instantly, my chest felt tight; I was sweating profusely, so I left the car and went back to my office, and then I started vomiting and almost passed out. My secretary called 911, and I ended up in the emergency room for a possible heart attack.

I remembered the ER doctor telling me my EKG was normal and that he had to run some tests after asking me a slew of questions. The hammer dropped on me when he came back and said something didn't make sense. He poignantly asked me again if I used any recreational drugs, which I adamantly denied. He looked at me with half scorn and half skepticism and said, "You lied to me, and I cannot trust you. You have cocaine in your system. I am glad I held back giving that medicine because it could have killed you with cocaine in your system." This was my lowest point ever. I was caught in my lie by a thoughtful, thorough ER doctor.

For once in my life, I was scared. Scared of losing my job, my health, relationships with my wife and children, and the prospect of everyone knowing that I was a drug abuser. I started sobbing profusely and begged the ER doctor not to include the drug use in my records. I pleaded and assured him that I would do anything to redeem myself. My job was my only lifeline, and if I lost the job, my family would suffer. The doctor looked at me and felt genuinely sorry for me and my actions. He shook his head and said, "Let me see what I can do," on his way out the door.

The doctor returned with redemption. He said he was going to help me, but his plan required a drastic measure. In exchange for not including cocaine use in my records, I had to check into a drug rehab facility that he helped facilitate. He diagnosed me with acute coronary syndrome, severe emotional distress, and major depression. Well, I checked into the facility received counseling, drug detoxification, and stress management coaching. When I left the facility after three weeks, I was a new person. I continued counseling for several weeks, and I eventually resigned from the job a few months later. I found a better job that allows me to spend time with my family and now function at a manageable stress level. My life is more purposeful and fulfilled, and I am drug and alcohol-free. Thanks to the ER doctor that gave me the opportunity to redeem myself.

As you can see from this story, we all deal with job-related stress, and the way we deal with the stressors can be deleterious, as in this story with eventual redemption. The problem is that we do not confront our stress head-on but rather look for ways to go around it.

It is important to understand and not underestimate the effect of stress. Everyone knows when they are stressed and the amount of stress they can handle without any deleterious effects. Having this understanding allows early mitigation before you fall on the side of the stress curve that is untenable. If you are dealing with stress, you can continue your current track or become stress-resistant by being decisive, setting priorities, limiting, or eliminating procrastination, and letting go of the idea of being a perfectionist (no one is perfect); pat yourself on the back now and then (it is okay), and by gosh, live an optimal lifestyle because the story is yours!

Financial stressors are common among physicians, healthcare providers, and a significant proportion of the population. The urge to maintain the so-called status quo of a physician's lifestyle is unavoidable for some, while others are able to maintain a balance. This category of stressor falls on the manageable stress bucket if you are so inclined to live within your means and not try to impress others. The consequence of financial stress asserts its effects on all aspects of well-being, but most importantly, on emotional and mental well-being.

Case Study:

Meet Dr. M. Plastics, a forty-six-year-old well-respected plastic surgeon. He has a very thriving practice, and his reputation precedes him. He lives in a multimillion-dollar residence in an exclusive gated neighborhood with an assortment of flashy cars (Ferrari, Rolls Royce, Porsche, Escalade). He is married to his second wife, who is a homemaker, and has three kids in private school. His monthly expenditure exceeds forty thousand dollars, and his practice is structured in a way that he has to generate revenue that exceeds that amount every month. He does not have his financial house in order. Although he makes good money, he has accumulated a lot of ongoing debt in an attempt to satisfy his insatiable lifestyle.

His life was relatively stressful due to financial stressors but manageable until the Covid-19 pandemic and everything shut down. As hospitals canceled all elective and non-essential surgical cases because of surges in Covid-19 cases and hospitalizations, most of his income-generating cases came to a dramatic halt. Consequently, the burden of his financial encumbrances is beginning to overwhelm him. He has become emotionally labile at home and work, berates nurses taking care of the few patients he has in the hospital, and had a recent blowout with the Hospital Administrator and the Chief Medical Officer over the cancellation of several previously scheduled abdominoplasty cases. This last incident led to the temporary suspension of his privileges and emergent meetings with the Medical Staff Leadership.

On the day of the meeting with the Medical Staff Leadership, Dr. Plastics was very apologetic and basically had a meltdown. He lamented how his income stream was at a standstill, how he had bills to pay, and right now, the inability to operate on his scheduled cases was going to put him in an uncomfortable financial situation. He apologized for his behavior, which he attributed to the overwhelming financial impact of the Covid-19 pandemic. He complained of not being able to sleep at night and constantly worrying about the ongoing situation's impact on his family and reputation. He indicated that his emotional state was in flux, and he didn't know what he was going to do if the situation didn't change.

Although the medical leadership was sympathetic to his plights, what piqued their interests was his emotional state, which they believed required immediate intervention. A concerted effort was made with his blessings to meet with the psychologist at the physician's well-being center for counseling sessions to help him navigate his troubles. Do you know anyone like Dr. Plastics? Are you gravitating towards becoming just like him? Is your financial house in order?

I have seen the likes of Dr. Plastics over the years, and I have had the privilege of counseling several. Financial stress on physicians or healthcare providers is generally not handled well. A balanced person should not find themselves in such a predicament. I understand the sacrifices we've made along the way and the urge to enjoy all the good things in life. However, it is also important to develop financial literacy and strive for some semblance of financial balance to avoid the unintended consequences of financial incompetence. Most physicians and healthcare providers who are not financially savvy need to have a financial advisor that can help ensure that your financial house is in order. Doing this allows you to still be able to live the life you desire while having a solid financial foundation and avoiding the emotional turmoil that Dr. Plastics experienced.

Planning for life requires strategy. Understanding the unintended consequences of our actions (in this case, financial indiscretion) can help us mitigate the outcome. The impact of stress on overall well-being cannot be overstated. However, understanding manageable stress and dealing with it effectively by utilizing all the available resources will enable us to control our story.

The story of Dr. Plastics is not unique. However, resources are available, such as the Physician Well-being Center and Medical Staff Leadership, which is structured to represent the physicians not just as adjudicators but also as proponents of the overall well-being of the medical staff members. Investments in such a structure will lead to successful interventions for any medical staff member on the verge of emotional breakdown, regardless of the inciting factors. Institutions seeking to ensure the well-being of their physicians and healthcare providers should consider investing in a robust medical staff leadership infrastructure and a dedicated Center for Physician well-being.

Feeding Your Thoughts: The Greatest (and Worst) Impact

Good nutrition is an integral component of a healthy lifestyle. A healthy, balanced diet that's augmented with physical activities will enable the maintenance of a healthy weight, reduce the propensity for chronic diseases, and simultaneously promote overall health. On the other hand, an unhealthy diet with a lack of physical activities has been well documented as preventable risk factors for obesity and non-communicable diseases such as stroke, cancer, heart disease, and diabetes, which together contributes to almost sixty percent of the leading causes of mortality in the world.

Case study:

Meet Dr. Justina Case. She is a thirty-eight-year-old dynamic Emergency Medicine Physician. She is a vibrant, athletic, nutritionally savvy doctor and beloved by all the team members and her patients. However, over the last eight months, she has slowly become withdrawn and appeared to put on forty pounds. She is easily fatigued when responding to a code, very short with the patients she is caring for, and her nutritional savviness is now substituted with unsavory condiments and fast foods. She was notorious for showing up to her shifts fifteen to thirty minutes early, but lately, she has been late to work several times during the past two months.

On one of the slow nights in the ER, she had revealed to one of the lead nurses who was a close acquaintance of hers about how she hated her job and the trepidation she felt coming to every shift. She indicated that her inactivity and changed dietary habits had led to a significant weight gain. Owing to these changes, she now has high blood pressure and early-onset diabetes. She does not exercise anymore, has no interest in things she used to be passionate about, and all she wants to do is stay indoors and eat after her shifts. Although the nurse leader was a close acquaintance, she was concerned about her friend's well-being that she felt compelled to bring these concerns to her immediate supervisor, who then notified the ED Medical director.

The case of Dr. Justina Case is an unfortunate one. A lot of physicians are suffering in silence with mental illness. She was contacted by leadership, and a meeting was convened. During the meeting, she confided that the last litigation she was involved in was the catalyst for her depressed state. She stated that although she did nothing wrong; she was devastated that the group settled the case on her behalf instead of fighting to clear her name. Since then, second-guessing herself is now the norm, she performs more patient workups than normal, and she is terrified of being sued again. She indicated the anxiety of coming to work and performing her duties as an emergency medicine physician is too overwhelming. She eats to calm her stress, and as a consequence; she is now overweight, hypertensive, and pre-diabetic. Fortunately, she was offered counseling sessions through the center for physician well-being, and she was able to turn things around and regain her health.

Although situations that affect our emotional state may arise, how we cope with such situations determines the effects on our well-being. Dr. Justina Case resorted to unhealthy dietary choices to cope with her mental health, which led to unintended consequences of obesity, hypertension, and early-onset diabetes.

Making healthy dietary choices is one of the many ways to ensure physical wellness, though such choices are often perceived as difficult to accomplish consistently. In a world that is so fast-paced, it is easy to succumb to the fast, easy, unhealthy, on-the-go diet options. To achieve a healthy eating lifestyle, it must be easy, simple, and deliberate. Being deliberate in this context is the understanding that when you are hungry, you are at the lowest point of energy, and you have to demonstrate significant self-control when deciding what to eat. It is important to understand that the proverbial adage "you are what you eat" remains true today because the food consumed exacts significant influences on mental alertness and concentration, level of energy, enhances a healthy immune system, and helps maintain a healthy weight.

If I rhetorically say that the food you eat affects the way your brain functions, would you believe me? Well, there is a preponderance of the evidence that shows that dietary factors exert effects on the brain that affect molecular events related to the management of the metabolism of energy and synaptic plasticity. In essence, energy metabolism influences neuronal formation, neuronal signaling, and synaptic plasticity, which ultimately affects mental health.[57] Recent studies[58] are beginning to provide evidence of the influence of dietary factors on specific molecular systems and the mechanism that maintains mental function.

Dietary fats are an integral part of brain functioning. Dietary lipids, specifically Omega-3 polyunsaturated fatty acids, are normal components of cell membranes and are essential for brain function. According to a research study that investigated the effects of long-chain polyunsaturated fatty acids on the development of normal brain functions,[59] diets rich in Omega-3 fatty acids support cognitive processes in humans. On the other hand, diets that are high in saturated fatty acids are notoriously implicated in the reduction of molecular substrates that support cognitive processes and increase the risk of neurological dysfunction in both humans and animals.[60] In essence, the fat you eat has a significant implication on the way your brain works.

Just as the food you eat impacts mental alertness and overall cognitive function, the more attentive you are by virtue of your diet can also determine your level of productivity. According to the International Labor Organization (ILO) study, inadequate nutrition, or diet on the job, is costing countries around the world up to twenty percent in lost productivity.[61] As healthcare providers, oftentimes, compensations are based on productivity. Personally, as an emergency medicine physician, most of my compensation is based on my productivity. If I am less productive, my overall earned income will decrease significantly, with a potential implication on my household's monthly budget (if I fall in the category of providers that have to hit certain dollar amounts every month to avert financial distress). This is an avoidable stressor that could be curtailed by subscribing to a proper dietary routine.

The brain is a dynamic organ that requires a constant supply of energy to maintain optimal performance. The energy source of the brain is glucose. Whatever food is ingested is eventually converted to glucose. The type of food you consume will determine the amount of glucose load in the bloodstream. If the food consumed produces a sudden surge in glucose levels, the energy production will be significant, with increased alertness and productivity that gradually wanes. This is the high and low phenomenon. Contrarily, food that slowly releases glucose to the bloodstream maintains a constant supply of energy and a consistent level of focus and productivity for a longer duration. This is where the concept of glycemic index appears.

The glycemic index is a value that is assigned to food based on how slowly or rapidly those foods produce an increase in blood glucose levels. This mostly refers to carbohydrates. Carbohydrates with low glycemic indexes are more slowly digested, absorbed, and metabolized, thus causing a lower and slower rise in blood glucose over a long duration. On the contrary, a high glycemic index carbohydrate is rapidly digested, absorbed, and metabolized while causing a higher and rapid rise in blood glucose for a short duration (Figure of GI). It is imperative to understand that for increased mental alertness and productivity, carbohydrates are an important staple in most diets, and choosing the right carbohydrates can enhance your mental and cognitive alertness and productivity.

At the end of the day, the goal is to eat healthily. A study published in the book *Willpower: Rediscovering the Greatest Human Strength* by the psychologist Roy F Baumeister further demonstrated that healthy eaters are more productive. In the study, researchers told children to skip breakfast before coming to school. Half the children were randomly selected to eat a nutritious breakfast while at school, and the rest were given nothing to eat. The study showed the children who had nutritious breakfasts had fewer behavioral problems and higher learning patterns than those who had not. However, when those who had not had breakfast were given snacks, their success improved as well. Just like the kids, eating the right meal or diet will determine the level of productivity at your workplace.

It is generally acceptable to surmise that healthy nutrition prevents avoidable non-communicable diseases like obesity, which is present in about 33.8 percent of U.S. adults. Eating the right number of healthy calories will enable the maintenance of a healthy weight. Maintaining a healthy weight protects the body from avoidable chronic diseases that arise as a complication of obesity. There are several dietary platforms out there to select from; choose the one that most suits your lifestyle that will enable you to maintain a healthy weight and a flourishing life.

A study titled, "On carrots and curiosity: eating fruits and vegetables is associated with greater flourishing in daily life" showed a relationship between the food we eat and flourishing life.[62] The researchers evaluated how food choices influence the daily experiences of participants. The participants were tasked with reporting food consumption, mood, and behavior over a thirteen-day period. The study showed that the more food and vegetables the participants consumed (up to seven servings daily), the happier, more engaged, and more creative they tended to be. The researchers theorized that fruits and vegetables contain the vital nutrients that promote the production of dopamine, a neurotransmitter that plays a key role in the experience of curiosity, motivation, and engagement. Additionally, fruits and vegetables provide antioxidants that minimize inflammation, improve memory, and enhance mood.

In a world that is so fast paced with constantly changing dynamics, we must stop and take control of our diets. Making healthy dietary choices has a significant impact on our overall physical well-being. To be successful in this endeavor, it has to be deliberate and not too complicated. Be familiar with food classes and dietary platforms that are available and choose the one that closely mirrors your lifestyle. At the end of the day, if you are able to accomplish this, you will be healthier, avoid non-communicable preventable diseases, stay mentally and cognitively sound, be more productive, maintain a healthy weight, and have a thriving, flourishing life that contributes to your overall physical well-being.

Time To Be Still: Relaxation

An important routine that everyone should attempt to carry out daily is the ability to relax. In a fast-paced world, we have the tendency to just keep going without taking time to exhale and just be still and free from tension or anxiety. According to the Oxford Dictionary, relaxation is "the state of being free from tension and anxiety." To maintain good physical health, we have to create a relaxation schedule to unwind from daily stress. Unmitigated stress overwhelms the nervous system, leading to the production of stress-response hormones. Persistent elevation of these hormones due to ongoing stress could have deleterious effects on the body's homeostasis. Taking the time to relax breaks the stress cycle and creates an environment of revitalizing tranquility.

The physiologic benefits of relaxation cannot be overstated. As humans, we all deal with functional stress in our lives, and this is what keeps us going. Stress beyond our optimal limit due to work demands, organizational inefficiencies, or relationship problems creates a state of distress. In this state, the production of stress-response hormones (such as glucocorticoids, catecholamines, growth hormones, and prolactin) gradually increases.[63] Recall the production of these hormones and their physiological effects (increased heart rates, elevated blood pressure, elevated blood glucose levels, increased respiratory rate, and excited brain activity) on the body that were discussed in the previous section. The ability to relax and the impact of the relaxation response are integral to counteract the effects of stress.

According to behavioral medicine pioneer Herbert Benson, MD, relaxation response is a physical state of deep rest that changes a person's physical and emotional response to stress.[64] Although Benson discovered relaxation response's power to reduce stress in the 1960s, his subsequent research revealed that the approach is no different from practices like praying, chanting, and repetitive motions that have been practiced over centuries. In his research titled, "Genomic Counter-Stress Changes Induced Relaxation Response," his team evaluated the effect of relaxation response on each of the forty thousand genes in the body and discovered that, when compared to the control group of the study, those who regularly used relaxation response produced more anti-oxidation and anti-inflammatory changes that counteracted the effects of stress on the human body.[65]

Evoking the relaxation response requires you to be in a relaxed state. In essence, the simple act of relaxing will evoke this response. According to Benson, "Anything that breaks the train of everyday thought will evoke this physiologic state (production of anti-oxidation and anti-inflammatory changes that counteracts the effects of stress on the body)." This physiological state is manifested through decreased heart rate, blood pressure, breathing, and muscle tension. A spa is an example of a place that induces this state. The setting is designed to provide a relaxing environment. From the time you walk through the doors, all your relaxation senses are stimulated by the music, the aromatic scents, and the serenity of the atmosphere.

Effective relaxation requires understanding easily applicable relaxation techniques. Although effortless modalities such as going for a walk, having a few minutes of quiet time to regroup, or weekly to monthly visits to the spa can suffice for most people, others require the next level of relaxation. Relaxation techniques are practices that help to accomplish full relaxation. These practices include but are not limited to the following: progressive relaxation, guided imagery, biofeedback, self-hypnosis, and deep breathing exercises. The overarching goal of these techniques is to stimulate the body's natural relaxation response that is represented by lowering the blood pressure, reducing the rate of breathing, and inducing a feeling of improved overall well-being.

Most of these relaxation techniques require the need of an expert or psychologist. However, for the layperson that wants to embark on daily relaxation, several modalities are also available. These modalities include deep breathing, progressive muscle relaxation, body scan meditation, visualization, self-massage, mindfulness meditation, rhythmic movement, mindful exercise, yoga, and tai chi.[66] The goal is to find the best relaxation technique that works for you. Remember, relaxation helps combat stress, and it is imperative that you activate the body's natural relaxation response to harness all the benefits to improve your well-being.

(Footnotes)

[21] Catherine M. Capio, et al, "Physical Well-Being."

[22] Kenneth R. Fox, *The Physical Self: from Motivation to Well-Being.*

[23] Ciro Conversano et al., "Optimism and Its Impact on Mental and Physical Well-Being."

[24] J. M. Ivancevich, et al, "Occupational Stress, Type A Behavior, and Physical Well Being."

[25] "Global Strategy on Diet, Physical Activity and Health."

[26] Pekka Oja and Sylvia Titze, "Physical Activity Recommendations for Public Health."

[27] R. R. Pate, "Physical Activity and Public Health."

[28] Ibid.

[29] D. E.R. Warburton, "Health Benefits of Physical Activity: the Evidence."

[30] Zeljko Pedisic et al., "Is Running Associated with a Lower Risk of All-Cause."

[31] "Brain Basics: Understanding Sleep."

[32] Ibid.

[33] "Circadian Rhythms."

[34] Tom Deboer, "Sleep Homeostasis and the Circadian Clock."

[35] Alexander A. Borbély and Peter Achermann, "Sleep Homeostasis and Models of Sleep Regulation."

[36] Carolin Reichert et al., "Sleep-Wake Regulation and Its Impact on Working Memory Performance."

[37] T J Balkin et al., "Sleep in America Poll."

[38] Giampiero Muccioli et al., "Neuroendocrine and Peripheral Activities of Ghrelin."

[39] Ibid.

[40] Guglielmo Beccuti and Silvana Pannain, "Sleep and Obesity."

[41] Karine Spiegel et al., "Brief Communication."

[42] Ioná Zalcman Zimberg et al., "Short Sleep Duration and Obesity."

[43] Julie D. Shlisky et al., "Partial Sleep Deprivation and Energy Balance in Adults."

[44] Orfeu M. Buxton and Enrico Marcelli, "Short and Long Sleep Are Positively Associated."

[45] Peter L. Franzen et al., "Cardiovascular Reactivity to Acute Psychological Stress."

[46] Xiaofan Guo et al., "Epidemiological Evidence for the Link between Sleep Duration."

[47] Michelle A. Short and Mia Louca, "Sleep Deprivation Leads to Mood Deficits"

[48] Yuki Motomura et al., "Two Days' Sleep Debt Causes Mood Decline."

[49] Zahid Saghir et al., "The Amygdala, Sleep Debt, Sleep Deprivation."

[50] "Stress in America Key Findings: 2010."

[51] David S Goldstein and Irwin J Kopin, "Adrenomedullary."

[52] Marian Joëls, "Corticosteroids and the Brain."

[53] Jill M. Mateo, "Inverted-U Shape Relationship."

[54] E. Ron de Kloet, Melly S. Oitzl, and Marian Joëls, "Stress and Cognition."

[55] Robert M. Yerkes and John D. Dodson, "The Relation of Strength of Stimulus."

[56] Marko Kesti, et al., "A Multidisciplinary Critical Approach to Measure."

[57] Fernando Gomez-Pinilla and Ethika Tyagi, "Diet and Cognition."

[58] Fernando Gómez-Pinilla, "Brain Foods."

[59] Joyce C McCann and Bruce N Ames, "Is Docosahexaenoic Acid."

[60] Carol E. Greenwood and Gordon Winocur, "High-Fat Diets."

[61] Christopher Wanjek, "Food at Work."

[62] Tamlin S. Conner et al., "On Carrots and Curiosity."

[63] Salam Ranabir and K Reetu, "Stress and Hormones."

[64] Herbert Benson, et al., "The Relaxation Response."

[65] Jeffery A. Dusek et al., "Genomic Counter-Stress Changes."

[66] Lawrence Robinson, "Relaxation Techniques for Stress Relief."

Chapter Six

The Second Pillar:
Emotional Well-Being

How is your emotional intelligence?

To understand this pillar, one needs to comprehend the definition of emotion. Emotion, as defined by the Merriam-Webster dictionary, is "a conscious mental reaction (such as anger, fear, pain, sorrow, hatred, love) subjectively experienced as a strong feeling directed towards a specific object and typically accompanied by physiological and behavioral changes in the body." To further grasp this concept, we need to understand the definition of feelings. It is any mental or physical response manifested as pleasure, pain, attraction, or repulsion. According to Keyes in the Encyclopedia of Gerontology, emotional well-being is the concept of balance between feelings (positive and negative) experienced in life and their perceived meanings (happiness and satisfaction).[67] Another concept from Vital Work Life described emotional well-being as characterized by a stable mood; ability to experience, manage and express emotions; acceptance of self and others; a positive outlook; and freedom from worry.[68]

To be emotionally well, you must be able to accept, manage feelings and subsequent behaviors, effectively cope with stress, and adapt to changes in a seamless fashion. Achieving this state requires both emotional regulation and intelligence. Emotional regulation is the capacity to exercise control over one's emotional state. Daily, we subconsciously utilize emotional regulation strategies to manage difficult situations. Strong emotional regulation skills allow one to deal with or cope with any situation in a positive manner. This is a skill that must be learned and practiced being readily exercised. It is the ultimate tool that allows one to cope with situations and enables the use of appropriate responses that do not evoke stress or fear. A solid emotional regulation skill can promote long-term well-being, improve work performance, enrich personal relationships, and lead to better overall health.[69]

Emotional intelligence (or Emotional Quotient, EQ) is defined as the ability to manage one's emotions and those of others or people around you. The Oxford English Dictionary defines it as "the capacity to be aware of, control, and express one's emotions, and to handle interpersonal relationships judiciously and empathetically." One of the most comprehensive, all-encompassing definitions was found in helpguide.org. It defines emotional intelligence as the ability to understand, use, and manage one's emotions in a positive way to relieve stress, communicate effectively, empathize with others, overcome challenges, and defuse conflicts.[70] Four proposed attributes promote a strong emotional intelligence: self-management (control impulsive feelings and behaviors), self-awareness (recognizing self-emotion and impacts on thoughts and behaviors), social awareness (demonstration of empathy), and relationship management (ability to develop and maintain good relationships).[71]

Emotional well-being requires balancing both positive and negative emotions and the ability to effectively utilize emotional regulation and emotional intelligence. In doing so, we can modulate responses to any stressful or uncomfortable situation. A person lacking in this dimension of well-being may exhibit labile, non-conforming behaviors that deviate from social norms.

Case Study:
Meet Dr. B. Cool. He is an accomplished hospitalist, very driven, embraces evidence-based medicine, and welcomes changes with infectious openness. Over the past two weeks, it was noted that he has been very labile, non-conciliatory, raising his voice, yelling at nurses, and short with his patients and colleagues. At one point, he got into a major argument on the phone at the nursing station, hurling profanity-laced insults to the receiver. This was brought to the attention of medical staff leadership, and he now has to meet with them to address his behaviors.

On meeting with Dr. Cool, it was apparent that he was overwhelmed and under an enormous level of stress. He indicated that all the metrics are driving him crazy, and no matter what he does, his metric scores are always in the toilet. He indicated he tried different approaches and was even shadowed by patient experience teams that gave him positive feedback, but his scores were always terrible. The tipping point for him was merit-based compensation and the fact that the new contract he just received tied the metrics that he believed had nothing to do with his clinical skills in managing his patients to his compensation. He admitted he's been extremely stressed out, and he just lost it when he received a call earlier that morning of the passing of his best friend. He accepted full responsibility for his outburst on the day in question, and he informed leadership that he had already started counseling to help him cope with his current state. Is Dr. B. Cool in a solid emotional well-being state? Does he need intervention? Now, let's dive deeper into the concept of emotional well-being.

Emotional well-being, as earlier stated, is characterized by a stable mood; ability to experience, manage, and express emotions; acceptance of self and others; a positive outlook; and freedom from worry. Simply speaking, it is a state of balance between positive and negative emotional states while effectively utilizing both emotion regulation and emotional intelligence. We all display both positive and negative emotions; however, extremes of emotion lead to a state of being unwell. According to the Mental Health Foundation, it is a positive sense of well-being that allows individuals to function in society and meet the rigors of everyday life. The kind of emotion you display will inadvertently affect your day-to-day functioning. Displaying a positive emotion attracts positive reactions, and like-minded people tend to gravitate together. If you emote positive emotions, you are often surrounded by positive-thinking people full of energy who are upbeat and eager to perform. On the contrary, constant displays of negative emotion led to isolation, loneliness, gravitation towards negatively minded people or the so-called naysayers.

Circling back to Dr. B. Cool's situation, it's apparent that he is going through an extreme work-related internal turmoil that tied his performance to compensation using metrics that he believed were unfair and did not represent his clinical performance and interactions with his patients. It appears he was trying to control his emotional state since emotions vary in intensity and duration. Having self-awareness of his emotions would have helped mitigate the outward displays of emotions he was exhibiting. The last straw appeared to be the phone call he received regarding the loss of his loved one. He obviously lost his emotional regulation, leading to the dysregulation that was exhibited by the outburst. His emotional intelligence during the outburst was lacking. Your emotional intelligence enables you to control your own emotions and those of others around you by creating an awareness of the impact of your emotional outbursts on others. It was noticeable that during the meeting, Dr. B. Cool was contrite and accepted full responsibility for his actions. He has also obviously reflected on the situation and sought counseling to help him navigate his way through his emotional quandary. He has already begun his intervention without prompt; this means he is on his way to bringing his emotions back to a balanced state and eventually improving both his emotion regulation and emotional intelligence.

Attaining a balanced emotional state or well-being requires the ability to maintain emotion at a crossroads of negative and positive fluctuations. The right emotional balance leads to the ability to learn from trauma and adversity, openness to emotional experience, clear values, and strong character, solid self-esteem, self-realization, passionate engagement, meaning and purpose in life, and positive and long-lasting relationships.

(Footnotes)

[67] C.L.M. Keyes, "Psychological Well-Being."

[68] Liz Ferron, "Emotional Well Being Definition."

[69] "Emotional Regulation: What Is It and Why Is It Important?"

[70] "Improving Emotional Intelligence (EQ)."

[71] Ibid.

Chapter Seven

The Third Pillar:
Mental Well-Being

Suffering in Silence.

This aspect of well-being is interconnected with emotional well-being. According to the World Health Organization, mental well-being is defined as a state of well-being in which the individual realizes his or her abilities, can cope with normal stresses of life, can work productively and fruitfully, and is able to make contributions to his or her community.[72] Simply speaking, our mental well-being relates to the way we feel or think about situations that confront us daily and how we cope or respond with the rigmarole of everyday life. Mental well-being should not be misconstrued as a mental health issue. Unlike mental health, mental well-being deals basically with the positive aspects of mental health.

With confusions between mental well-being and mental health, there have been several studies to adequately define what mental health really represents. According to a publication in *World Psychiatry Journal*, "Mental health is a dynamic state of internal equilibrium which enables individuals to use their abilities in harmony with universal values of society. Basic cognitive and social skills; ability to recognize, express, and modulate one's own emotions, as well as empathize with others; flexibility and ability to cope with adverse life events and function in social roles, and harmonious relationship between body and mind represent important components of mental health which contributes, to varying degrees, to the state of internal equilibrium."[73]

Mental health is much deeper than mental well-being. While mental well-being emphasizes self-actualization, positive stress response, productive life, and contribution to society, mental health encompasses emotional, psychological, and social well-being. Mental well-being is an integral part of the 5 Pillars of Well-Being. Being mentally well enables individuals to thrive in relationships both at home and work, live a productive life, respond positively to life stressors, and be able to be altruistic for the benefit of the community or society at large.

Case Study:

Dr. K. Love is a young, dynamic ER doctor, though the past two weeks have been particularly unusual; on most days, she is one of the fastest and most productive in the emergency department. She is always sharply dressed, arriving on time with a bright smile that lights up the room, and is loved by nurses and colleagues. Lately, though, she has been late to work on three occasions, her radiant smiles are nowhere to be found, her work efficiency has suffered, and she has received a couple of complaints from patients about her tone and her approach to care. Some of the nurses also noticed these dramatic changes and brought this to the attention of the facility medical director.

So why is this dynamic young physician exhibiting these dramatic changes? On meeting with the medical director, she divulged that she had been under enormous work-related stress. She indicated that the patients she has been seeing are unusually sicker than normal, and she has had to terminate resuscitations on four patients, including a three-year-old drowning victim. These events took a significant toll on her psyche and self-confidence to the extent that she started second-guessing herself. She concluded it's just hard to cope with all these deaths. The medical director empathized with her, provided her with the necessary resources, and recommended she seek consultation from the physician support services. Additionally, the medical director offered to have her next few shifts covered for her to take at least two weeks off to get needed help.

What this case demonstrated is a clinician that is emotionally drained, and as a result, her mental well-being is suffering. She has become less productive and inefficient, unable to cope or respond positively to life stressors, which inadvertently affected her relationship with patients and nursing staff. What is also apparent is that life events that are beyond our control have a significant impact on overall mental well-being. However, the way we respond to these situations determines the extent of their impact.

The question now is how do we improve mental well-being? In order to improve your overall mental well-being, it is important to understand how to take inventory of your mental well-being. There are several tools out there to measure mental well-being; however, the Warwick-Edinburgh Mental Well-Being Scale (WEMWBS), developed and validated in the U.K., is the one that stood out for its simplicity and ease of use. It is a short, psychometrically robust scale that has no ceiling effects on the sample population and measures mental well-being by focusing entirely on the positive aspects of mental health.[74]

After performing the exercise, the next step is to become familiar with ways to improve your mental well-being. There are several ways to accomplish this, depending on the source utilized. Some examples are to remove or reduce stress, build mental resilience, practice mindfulness, build or strengthen relationships or connect with other people, be physically active, learn new skills, and give to others. I have discussed physical activities and stress management earlier; building relationships, giving to others, and learning new skills are pretty straightforward. Building mental resilience and practicing mindfulness are concepts I would like to introduce here.

What is mental resilience? The word "mental" relates to your thoughts or thinking process and mind, and "resilience" means the capacity to recover quickly from difficulties or toughness. In essence, mental resilience is the ability of our mind and thought processes to rebound quickly or adjust accordingly to any stressful situation. Adaptability is the magic word here—the ability of a person to adapt successfully to the trials and tribulations of life when confronted with these challenges. Adaptability is a mental toughness that is developed over time, though it can also be learned. Having the intestinal fortitude to withstand stressors that challenge us daily is one of the essential attributes of physicians. Despite this attribute, though, we are all human and can be overwhelmed at any given time. However, having the understanding that it is totally okay to ask for help is the absolute first step to developing mental toughness. Unfortunately for most healthcare providers, ego seems to get in the way, owing to the perceived weakness associated with seeking help. This is where we have to get off our high horse and understand that the road to redemption starts with the first step. In this case, asking for help.

To be mentally resilient or tough, you have to be able to roll with the punches, absorb shocks that you can mentally handle, and pause when you are in over your head and seek guidance. When you are overwhelmed or mentally drained, pressing the pause button is very important because you are at a crossroad, and the path you embark upon after pressing the pause button determines the successful navigation of your challenges. Pressing the pause button allows you to perform a critical appraisal of your mental stressors and strategize how to address them with surgical precision. Remember, you are not alone, and you don't have to do it alone. If part of your strategy requires you to seek help (you know you do), just do it. This might save you a lot of pain, emotional energy, and wasted productivity. Lastly, seeking help is not a sign of weakness but strength.

Earlier in the book, I discussed strategies to address stressors. I mentioned identifying or taking inventory of the stressors, arranging them in terms of seriousness, identifying the ones you can do something about, and channeling your mental energy to the ones in this category. There are absolutely no gains in ruminating over things that are beyond your control. Having a clear focus relating to approaches to stressors is one of the foremost integral attributes of mental resilience or toughness. Acquiring this attribute allows you to seamlessly navigate the ebbs and flows of life. While obtaining this attribute is great, it is useless if you do not have the intestinal fortitude to press the pause button in the first place.

Activating the pause button is easier said than done. To trigger this button, you must be aware that something is wrong. This self-awareness is where mindfulness comes into play. What is mindfulness? According to the Oxford Dictionary, it is "a mental state achieved by focusing one's awareness on the present moment, while calmly acknowledging and accepting one's feelings, thoughts, and bodily sensations, used as a therapeutic technique." Further simplified from the site mindful.org, "It is the basic human ability to be fully present, aware of where we are and what we are doing, and not overly reactive or overwhelmed by what's going on around us."[75] In essence, we all possess mindfulness as one of our inherent qualities, and being able to access it when needed allows us to press the proverbial pause button.

So why is mindfulness important? Mindfulness has been extensively studied, and its implication on overall well-being is apparent. Correlational, quasi-experimental, and laboratory studies by Brown et al.,[76] using the Mindful Attention Awareness Scale (MAAS), concluded that: "MAAS measures a unique quality of consciousness that is related to a variety of well-being constructs, which differentiates mindfulness practitioners from others, and that it is associated with enhanced self-awareness. Furthermore, an experience sampling study shows that dispositional and state mindfulness both predict self-regulated behavior and positive emotional states."[77] The ability to create enhanced self-awareness using inherent mindfulness characteristics enables us to recognize when to press the pause or rest button.

Practicing mindfulness is something we ought to be doing daily. It has significant positive psychological effects on our overall outlook, increases subjective well-being, reduces psychological symptoms and emotional reactivity, and improves behavioral regulation.[78] Additionally, mindfulness practices help with the alleviation of life stressors and sufferings through clearly identifying root causes and decoupling them from habitual responses.[79]

Circling back, mental well-being is interwoven with our emotional well-being. Achieving balance in this stratosphere of well-being is an integral step towards wholeness. Developing mental and psychological resilience and the ability to understand and embrace mindfulness techniques will give you the seamless ability to press the proverbial pause button. Pressing this button helps us rest, recognize the moment, and be present with deliberate situational awareness that allows identification of the causes of strain to our mental health and well-being. Identifying these stressors opens the window to strategies that help manage them effectively while being mindful that we may require help doing so. It is very important to refute the stigma that asking for help projects weakness, and instead, you can decide to embrace the belief that seeking help is a window to a new reality of wealth of psychological benefits that include but are not limited to, reduction in stress and distress, and improvement of overall well-being.

(Footnotes)

[72] Helen Herrman, et al.,
Promoting Mental Health.

[73] Silvana Galderisi et al., "Toward a New Definition of Mental Health."

[74] Ruth Tennant et al., "The Warwick-Edinburgh Mental Well-Being Scale."

[75] Mindful Staff et al., "What Is Mindfulness?"

[76] Kirk Warren Brown and Richard M. Ryan, "The Benefits of Being Present."

[77] Andrew Hafenbrack, et al. "Debiasing the Mind through Meditation."

[78] Shian-Ling Keng, et al., "Effects of Mindfulness on Psychological Health."

[79] J. Brewer, "Mindfulness."

Chapter Eight

The Fourth Pillar:
Spiritual Well-Being

Does your daily life have purpose?

In order to discuss spiritual health, it is imperative to understand the term spirituality. Spirituality means different things to different people, depending on their background and personal experiences. For some people, it relates to religious affiliations or beliefs, while for others, religion has no bearing when it comes to spirituality. It is more about the exploration of our desire for purpose, meaning, and interconnectedness with others and nature. Spirituality definitions vary depending on beliefs. While Christianity refers to spirituality as a set of beliefs, values, and way of life that reflects the teachings of the Bible, the Buddhists refer to spirituality as "Shamata," which means tranquil abiding or living, while the Hindus refer to it as relating to people's deepest thoughts and beliefs. The majority of the Far East traditions consider spirituality as the search to understand your real self, find the true nature of consciousness, and gain spiritual awakening.

There have been varied attempts to define spirituality, but most are fraught with controversies. Current definitions range from the spectrum of religious to humanistic constructs. Defining spirituality requires the understanding that it must be multifaceted. In the Oxford English Dictionary, at least twenty-four separate meanings of the word spirit are listed. It has been universally reported in the literature that spirituality is at the heart of the human experience[80] and is experienced by everyone.[81] It is generally believed that everyone has spiritual needs; however, it is also claimed that "human spirituality unifies the whole person, and it is an inbuilt feature of the human species that develop from the beginning of an individual's life (or not) depending on prevailing conditions."[82, 83]

The term spirituality is dynamic. Its unique essence must be felt before it can be conceptualized.[84] Using this perspective, terms like "spiritual growth" and "development" are used to express the vibrant nature of spirituality.[85] According to an article published by John Fisher,[86] "Spirituality is concerned with a person's awareness of the existence and experience of inner feelings and beliefs which gives purpose, meaning, and value to life. It helps individuals to live at peace with themselves, to love (God, if religious) their neighbor, and to live in harmony with the environment."

Now that we have grasped the understanding of spirituality, we can now begin the conversation on spiritual well-being. What is spiritual well-being, and how is it related to overall well-being? Just like spirituality, there appear to be several definitions or explanations for spiritual well-being. according to a paper by Ellison, "Spiritual well-being arises from an underlying state of spiritual health and is an expression of it, much like the color of one's complexion, and pulse rate are expressions of good physical health."[87] Following this construct, Fehring et al., described spiritual well-being as an indication of individuals' quality of life in the spiritual dimension or simply an indication of spiritual health.[88]

Spiritual well-being is about our life and relationship to the wider world. According to a recently published article by Ghaderi et al., "Spiritual health includes purposeful life, transcendence, and actualization of different dimensions and capacities of a human being. It creates a balance between physical, psychological, and social aspects of human life."[89] Simply speaking, spiritual well-being means a purposeful life. It provides us with the ethos of faith, beliefs, values, ethics, principles, and morals that guide our ways of life.

To be spiritually well, we must possess the ability to experience and integrate meaning and purpose in life through our connectedness with self, others, arts, music, literature, nature, or a power greater than ourselves. Spiritual well-being should not be misconstrued with religious beliefs; however, it is the central feature of people of religious faith. Individual spiritual well-being is significantly impacted by the community they associate with and their relationship with that community. In essence, to be spiritually well, you must have a positive engagement with others, yourself, and the environment.[90]

The context of well-being is an interconnected Rubik's cube. Spiritual health and well-being have a significant interrelationship with psychological well-being. Balanced spiritual health fosters psychological health. A recently published article that evaluated the relationship between spirituality, health-related behavior, and psychological well-being demonstrated that both spirituality and health-related behaviors are positively related to psychological well-being and that the relationship with spirituality is also mediated by health-related behaviors. In the subset of the study, spirituality displays a stronger relationship with psychological well-being.[91]

Case Study:
Dr. Bonkers is a newly hired general surgeon just out of residency. He is bright, charming, and beloved by all. He is very outgoing and humble. Within eight months of employment, the perception of this charming doctor has changed. He is now perceived as egotistical, arrogant, belittles his residents on rounds, and displays some unethical behaviors. His problems started when some nurses found out he was dating four different nurses from different units in the hospital simultaneously. Things that were normally overlooked by the nursing staff generated complaints. He was accused of abusing opioids and compromising patient care by secretly stealing patients' medicines because he was found sleeping in an empty patient room and was difficult to awaken. This eventually reached leadership.

During the investigation, it was discovered that on several occasions, when performing sedation or medicating patients for bedside procedures, he often asked the nurses to let him administer the medications. In doing so, he usually administered less medication to the patients and often told nurses that they did not need all of it, resulting in him wasting the remaining medication in the sink. Apparently, he was self-medicating with the opioids. Additionally, it was brought to the attention of leadership that Dr. Bonkers was found in a compromising situation with an unknown female employee in the physicians' parking area.

On meeting with Dr. Bonkers, the salacious details were excluded with a focus on his self-medication and opioid dependency. He alluded that the last few months had been stressful because he felt the nurses were out to get him. He said they complained about every little thing pertaining to him and called him unnecessarily in the middle of the night to ask for Tylenol orders or other mundane things that could wait until the morning. He said that for him to deal with the stress and the coordinated nursing attacks, he started self-medicating with opioids. He indicated he had only done it a few times and that the last time was when he was found sleeping in the patient's room. Dr. Bonkers said that he was up all night with incessant calls from multiple nursing units and that when he started his rounds in the morning, he was so tired that he had to take something to help him function. However, he said he must have taken the wrong drug because what he remembered was someone shaking him vigorously in an attempt to wake him up. He basically confessed to using drugs and that he was dependent and needed help. His case was then referred to the physicians health advisory council for adjudication.

What is wrong with this picture? Do you know a Dr. Bonkers? Should these events destroy his career, or should he be given a chance to rehabilitate? What do you think of his spiritual well-being? Does it appear that he is spiritually well? Let's take a quick look at the qualities that make a person spiritually well.

To be considered spiritually well, a person needs to subscribe to some kind of belief, faith, values, ethical standards, principles, and morals that guide their way of life. Has this doctor demonstrated that he has any moral values or principles (engaging in relationships with several staff members simultaneously) or common medical ethical standards (underdosing patients and keeping the rest to himself)? He obviously has not; otherwise, he would not have engaged in such immoral actions.

Suffice it to say that this provider is spiritually challenged. Someone that is spiritually well is incorruptible because they have a sense of belonging, which leads to the tendency to exhibit honesty at all times and care for others. A person that cares for others like their family will not compromise the medication of suffering patients to satisfy their personal desires. Similarly, a person that is spiritually grounded will not intentionally dilute chemotherapy drugs intended for suffering cancer patients for monetary gains. Some decisions we make in medicine require us to be principled, ethically sound, and exhibit morality. These attributes are all part of the components needed to be spiritually grounded.

Once again, spirituality should not be misconstrued with religion. A person can be spiritual and not subscribe to any religious affiliations. Spirituality is living a full, purposeful life derived from feeling interconnected with something bigger than yourself. It aligns your core with the sense of belonging and the urge to contribute to the community as a whole. Being spiritually well means you are principled, have some faith and beliefs, are morally sound, and ethical in all your endeavors. A spiritually well healthcare provider is highly motivated and seeks to constantly provide the best care to all patients while simultaneously showing care and concern for colleagues and all care-team members.

Spiritual Core

So, how do you attain healthy spiritual wellness or a state of spiritual well-being? Well, it starts with the understanding that one's values, principles, beliefs, and a sense of purpose are instrumental to arriving at this state. This is the most personal piece of the wellness pillars because of its overarching goal of life with meaning and purpose. There are several ways to improve your spiritual health; what I believe to be the most important starting point is to explore your spiritual core—taking an introspective inventory of yourself by asking the following questions: Who am I? What do I value most? What is my purpose in life? The exploration of these questions will enable you to understand an in-depth perspective of yourself that will allow you to begin your journey into spiritual wellness.

Deeper Meaning

While understanding your spiritual core is what I believe to be the fundamental foundation to begin your spiritual health journey, looking for a deeper meaning in life will make the journey to spiritual health more meaningful. Looking deeper is a transcendental way of viewing things around you. Looking deeper keeps your focus on things that are actually more important than just material things. It allows you to compartmentalize your life with the ability to let go of things that are irrelevant while having a renewed focus on things that will allow you to find your purpose in life. Looking deeper as you journey through life with all its trials and tribulations allows you to extricate yourself from all the distractions while focusing on meaningful things.

Gratitude

Spiritual health needs to be sustained, just like your overall well-being. One of the ways to sustain this is to practice gratitude. The word gratitude has a different connotation depending on the resources. A general practical definition is a state of thankfulness and showing appreciation for what is valuable and meaningful to oneself.[92] According to Harvard Medical School, gratitude enhances the development of positive emotions, allows you to relish good experiences, improves health, deals with adversity, and builds strong relationships. One of the simplest ways to practice gratitude is to keep a gratitude journal and perform an exercise such as writing down five things that you are grateful for on a daily basis. The element of reflection inherent in being grateful helps establish and maintain spiritual health.

Meditation

The ability to escape it all and be still is another way to enhance your spiritual health. One of the ways to take a break and refocus your inner core energy is to meditate. Meditation is one of the simplest ways to sustain your spiritual health. The monks use meditation to achieve spiritual enlightenment. According to the Merriam-Webster Dictionary, the purpose of meditation is to engage in a mental exercise (such as concentration on one's breathing or repetition of a mantra) for the purpose of reaching a heightened level of spiritual awareness.

The exact origin of meditation is hard to pinpoint, as archeologists found different iterations of meditation with religious practices in ancient Egypt and China, as well in Judaism, Hinduism, and Buddhism.

The benefits of meditation cannot be overstated. It lowers stress levels, increases emotional health, boosts self-awareness, and improves focus. A study published by Harvard Medical School professor Dr. Herbert Benson demonstrated that people who meditate used seventeen percent less oxygen had lowered heart rates and produced increased brainwaves that could help with sleep.[93] The ability to meditate and be in tune with your mind allows you to be in a state of quiescent spiritual introspection and is a sure way to enhance your spiritual health. There are several popular types of meditation (mindfulness, spiritual, focused, movement, mantra, transcendental, progressive relaxation, loving-kindness, and visualization), and it is imperative to understand that one size does not fit all. You need to identify which mediation practices best suits your lifestyle.

Mindfulness

As we continue on the spiritual journey, we have to continuously cultivate habits to sustain our spiritual health. Another modality to help us maintain our spiritual health is to practice mindfulness, as discussed in the previous chapter. Unlike meditation, which is an intentional practice for a certain amount of time designed to train your brain, like working out at the gym to strengthen a muscle, mindfulness is putting your meditation into practice by being present in your everyday life.

Mindfulness could be referred to as a mirror image of meditation that deals with an intense awareness of feelings at the moment without interpretations and judgments. So why is it important? Well, it allows us to refocus on the present moment. Focusing on the present moment is synonymous with pressing the proverbial "pause button" discussed earlier.

Practicing mindfulness allows you to be fully engaged because the priority is focused on the present instead of the past or future. Presently, as we deal with the current Covid-19 pandemic or any overtly stressful situation, mindfulness becomes extremely important, as it allows us to be intentional about creating space to recharge and remind ourselves about what is important. The intentionality inherent in the practice prevents us from being preoccupied with the unwanted emotional upheaval that could undermine the state of harmony we are trying to achieve. Be mindful of who you are, where you are, and where you are going, and practice mindfulness daily to enhance your spiritual health.

Yoga

Another common way to sustain your spiritual health is the practice of yoga. Yoga is closely intertwined with meditation. It emphasizes the importance of regular acts of meditation because of its impact on effecting positive thoughts. The effects of this ancient practice on spiritual health are predicated on the seven spiritual laws that students of yoga embrace. Interestingly enough, these seven laws are woven into the fabric of each yoga practice and movement.

According to the book published by Deepak Chopra and David Simon titled: *The Seven Spiritual Laws of Yoga*, the seven principles of yoga are: law of pure potentiality, law of giving and receiving, law of karma, law of least effort, law of intention and desire, law of detachment, and the law of dharma. These principles speak for themselves. The movements of yoga are spiritual and require some learning to avoid injury. The sheer focus and ability to be completely detached and isolate yourself in a spiritual realm is powerful. If you have never tried yoga, it would be hard to conceptualize. However, if you are a yoga buff, you have a complete understanding of these feelings.

Although the physical benefits of yoga (improved flexibility, enhanced balance, superb endurance, improved immune function, and better balance) are impressive, the deeper connection to the spirit and the gift of a calm mind during duress or chaos is what brings you closer to your spiritual health. For those that understand the essence of yoga, the union of the mind, body, and spirit is very important. It enhances your mind and body integration through exercises such as conscious breathing, physical postures, and movements that bring you to your spiritual core. Practicing yoga equips you with a heightened sense of awareness, ingenuity, perception, creativity, and inventiveness. If the art of yoga piques your interest as a means of enhancing your spiritual health, look for beginner's yoga that suits your lifestyle.

Spiritual health is an integral part of the five pillars of well-being. Being spiritually well enhances your emotional wellness, which inextricably promotes overall physical wellness. Developing your spiritual health and nurturing and sustaining it using some of the modalities described above will get you to a state of spiritual wholeness or well-being.

(Footnotes)

[80] Philippa Wheeler, "Spirituality & Health Multidisciplinary Explorations."

[81] Peter Nolan and Paul Crawford, "Towards a Rhetoric of Spirituality in Mental Health Care."

[82] Andrew Oldnall, "A Critical Analysis of Nursing."

[83] David Hay, K. Helmut Reich, and Michael Utsch, "Spiritual Development."

[84] Jack G. Priestley, "Towards Finding the Hidden Curriculum."

[85] Larry S. Chapman, "Developing a Useful Perspective on Spiritual Health."

[86] John Fisher, "The Four Domains Model."

[87] Craig W. Ellison, "Spiritual Well-Being."

[88] R J Fehring, J F Miller, and C Shaw, "Spiritual Well-Being."

[89] Ahmad Ghaderi et al., "Explanatory Definition of the Concept of Spiritual Health."

[90] Ritika Srivastava, "Spiritual Wellbeing at Work: How to Do It Right."

[91] Agnieszka Boźek, et al. "The Relationship Between Spirituality."

[92] Joshua A. Rash, et al., "Gratitude and Well-Being."

[93] Herbert Benson, *The Relaxation Response.*

Chapter Nine

The Fifth Pillar:
Social Well-Being

The best way to complete yourself (which has nothing to do with you).

Humans are social by nature. Our social interactions are essential to every facet of our health. This social nature is the foundation for relationships, associations, communities, and societies. The need to be social drives us to live in families, communities, seek the company of others, and form relationships. According to the Dalai Lama XIV, "We human beings are social beings. We survive here in dependence on others. Whether we like it or not, there is hardly a moment in our lives when we do not benefit from others' activities. For this reason, it is hardly surprising that most of our happiness arises in the context of our relationships with others."

According to the philosopher Aristotle, human beings are social animals that naturally seek the companionship of others as part of their well-being. Also, the bestselling author, surgeon, and public health researcher that I greatly admire, Atul Gawande, stated that, "Human beings are social creatures. We are social, not just in the trivial sense that we like company and not just in the obvious sense that we depend on each other. We are social in a more elemental way: simply to exist as a normal human being requires interaction with others." In essence, being social is what allows us to have a strong network of support or strong community bonds that foster both emotional, psychological, and physical health.

The link between being social and overall well-being has been extensively researched. A study titled: "Social Skills and the Stress-Protective Role of Social Support" by Cohen et al., evaluated incoming college freshmen and demonstrated that social support was effective in reducing depression in both those who have healthy self-esteem and those with poor self-image.[94] As we age gracefully, the importance of social relationships and involvement cannot be overstated. A European study based on the data from the Survey of Health, Aging and Retirement in Europe (SHARE) that included eleven European countries and 22,000 households showed that Europeans over the age of fifty that participated in social or community activities were more likely to report good or very good health.[95] The buffering hypothesis by Cohens, et al. suggests that, "Social relationships may provide resources (informational, emotional, or tangible) that promotes adaptive behavioral or neuroendocrine responses to acute or chronic stressors (e.g., illness, life events, life transitions). The aid from social relationships thereby moderates or buffers the deleterious influence of stressors on health."[96]

Additionally, several other studies have shown the implications of social relationships and mortality. In a meta-analytic review by Holt-Lunstad et al., an actual or perceived social isolation is associated with an increased risk of early mortality.[97] Similarly, House JS, et al., also stated that, "Social relationships, or the relative lack thereof, constitute a major risk factor for health—rivaling the effect of well-established health risk factors such as cigarette smoking, blood pressure, blood lipids, obesity, and physical activity."[98] These studies demonstrated that social interactions and relationships are important to both our psychological health and mortality. As a matter of fact, the World Health Organization now recognizes social relationships as an important determinant of health throughout our lives.

Just as social relationships and interactions have implications on psychosocial health, studies are now consistently showing significant impacts on modifiable health risk factors. A recent meta-analysis that included eleven longitudinal studies on cardiovascular disease and eight on stroke suggested that social isolation and loneliness were associated with a thirty-percent excess risk of an incident in coronary heart disease and stroke.[99] A similar study by Hakulinen C, et al. also demonstrated that isolated and lonely persons are at increased risk of acute myocardial infarction and stroke, and among those with a history of AMI and stroke, increased risk of death. Most of these risks were explained by conventional risk factors.[100]

Overwhelming evidence suggests that humans are social by nature and that being social is part of our innate attributes and affects every aspect of our lives, emotionally, mentally, physically, and psychologically. What then is social well-being? According to *Psychology Today*, social well-being is "the ability to communicate, develop meaningful relationships with others, and maintain a support network that helps you overcome loneliness."[101] Simply put, social wellness involves the building of wholesome, nurturing, and supportive relationships as well as cultivating an authentic connection with those around you. The fact that we not only crave social interactions, and those studies show that we require them for our overall health makes social well-being an essential component of the five pillars of well-being.

In order to be socially well, we have to have the ability to maintain meaningful relationships with friends, neighbors, family, and colleagues in the work environment. Maintaining these relationships requires some modicum of values that allows you to conduct yourself in an acceptable social standard that includes good communication skills, respecting yourself and others, being altruistic, and engaging in activities that contribute to your community.

As a healthcare provider, executive, or someone involved in executive-level leadership positions or roles in any industry, the demands of the job and the need to be beyond reproach tend to isolate us from things that matter. I recalled my wife telling me a while ago that I needed to socialize more, go out, hang out with my friends. I couldn't just be a homebody; "Have friends over sometimes so your kids could know your friends and see their father not just as Daddy or a doctor, but someone that has relationships outside of the home." I remembered how giddy my kids got when a friend or a colleague came to the house. My daughter once asked, "Daddy! Do you have any friends?" This hit me at my core and brought me to the realization that I had been living life in a bubble that revolved around my immediate family and that I had not made attempts to cultivate any kind of true friendship with anyone. Interacting with colleagues at work is one thing, but cultivating a true relationship or friendship is a completely different thing. I realized I had no one to even call to pour my heart out to other than my wife. I had no true social network or interconnectedness. I was living in isolation. Wow!

This narrative had to change if I really wanted to be whole and have a superb overall well-being. So, what did I have to do? I started to follow through on conversations that ended with "Let's grab a bite or a drink sometime," or the ones that ended with an invitation to play golf or tennis. Ordinarily, these invitations never received a follow-up. But now that I am intentional, I am out playing tennis, golfing, biking, running, and exploring my passions with social acquaintances. With each outing, I started building meaningful relationships, social networks, and developing true friendships. From these networks, opportunities to participate or volunteer in the community on a bigger scale materialized, and I started to have an increased sense of belonging to the community. I developed some semblance of social acceptance, satisfying feelings of contributing to the community, some social coherence, and the feelings of full integration into the society in which I was once living in isolation.

A publication in the *American Sociological Association* by Corey Keyes[102] proposed five elements of social well-being that I discovered to be extremely useful in my journey to social wellness. Understanding these elements and applying them during the phase of self-introspection adequately provided the tools needed to achieve a healthy social well-being. What are these five elements?

1. Social integration is the evaluation of the quality of one's connection to society and community. It is asserted that those individuals that are healthy feel that they are part of society. As individuals, we have commonality with others in our community or social reality, and to some extent, the degree that we feel that we belong to the society is what constitutes integration. A typical example could be a move to a new neighborhood or starting a new job or relocating to a new country. The innate things that we naturally do are to get a feel for our community, coworkers, or neighborhood in order to see how we fit into the new environment.

2. Social acceptance is predicated on the understanding of the characteristics and qualities of the people in the community. Understanding the community influences the generalizable view or perception of the community. This perception (if positive) allows an individual to have favorable views and trust and accept others. Trusting and accepting others is tantamount to self-acceptance. According to Keyes, "Social acceptance is the social analog to personal acceptance." In essence, people who feel good and accept themselves tend to exemplify good mental health and social well-being.

3. Social contribution is based on the premise of doing something or contributing to the generalizable good of the community or society. This is the appraisal of our inherent social values. This value emanates from the belief that we are vital members of society with something to offer to the betterment of the community. Doing something or being involved in the community fills the wellness cup. There are several ways to be involved in the community (volunteering, mentoring, philanthropic activities, etc.), but individuals need to determine the best way to contribute to the generalizable good of society

4. Social actualization is the realization that society has the potential to benefit all, which is accomplished by citizens and organizations. Understanding that a better society is better for all encourages participation in activities that benefit society. According to Keyes, "Socially healthier people can envision that they, and people like them, are potential beneficiaries of social progress and growth." A progressive society is driven by like-minded people or organizations working together to accomplish a shared vision. Looking introspectively to see the potential for progress in our communities stimulates the need to be engaged with like-minded citizens to cultivate societal potentials.

5. Social coherence is the idea of coming together, though we may be different, and working together for the good of humanity—contrary to social cohesion that promotes sticking together under a single identity and conforming in times of crisis or turmoil. It allows us to discover common values and humanity through working together without engaging in discussions about our differences. It is a stable, harmonious relationship between individuals who share common interests and objectives. In a socially coherent society, each individual is self-regulated by their own inherent values and moral ethos, and they function towards a shared interest. An individual that is not self-regulated may act in opposition to shared interests, favoring their own personal interests. This will create social incoherence.

The above-listed five elements of social well-being have been studied and deemed to be instrumental as a guide. Social well-being is an integral component of overall well-being. Gaining an insight into ways to attain balance in this pillar of well-being is extremely beneficial to both emotional and mental health. When in a healthy state, this pillar creates a sense of belonging and the fulfillment of a purposeful life. According to an anonymous author, "If I die today and I had three very good friends, I have lived a wonderful life." Being socially well is not a difficult task to accomplish; it just requires intentionality and the willingness to be connected and utilize tools provided in this segment to allow you to accomplish this goal. Social wellness affirms the realization that no man or woman is an island. We all need social interactions to complete us and have a fulfilling life. A deliberate attempt to cultivate habits that foster social relationships and interactions can be extremely beneficial for your overall well-being.

(Footnotes)

[94] Sheldon Cohen, et al."Social Skills and the Stress-Protective Role of Social Support."

[95] Nicolas Sirven and Thierry Debrand, "Social Participation and Healthy Ageing."

[96] Sheldon Cohen, et al., "Social Relationships and Health."

[97] Julianne Holt-Lunstad et al., "Loneliness and Social Isolation as Risk Factors for Mortality."

[98] J. House, K. Landis, and D Umberson, "Social Relationships and Health."

[99] Nicole K Valtorta et al., "Loneliness and Social Isolation as Risk Factors."

[100] Christian Hakulinen et al., "Social Isolation and Loneliness as Risk Factors."

[101] Tchiki Davis, "What Is Well-Being?"

[102] Corey Lee Keyes, "Social Well-Being."

Chapter Ten

Living Proof

Final thoughts that are personal to me.

Life's journey always starts with the first step. Starting the journey without a concise plan doesn't mean you will fail to get to your destination; you will probably just waste a lot of precious time along the way. The ability to adapt is an inherent attribute of humans by nature, and it allows us to respond to changes in our environment. The only thing in life that is constant is change, and the resistance to change renders you irrelevant and obsolete. It is important that as we embark on life's journey, we have to be willing to change with the ebbs and flows.

The dynamics in healthcare that frustrated me to the extent that I contemplated walking away from medicine resulted from a barrage of changes and regulations that I believed impeded my ability to practice medicine to my full capacity. As I watched several colleagues transition to early retirement or cash-based concierge medicine, I also witnessed others become overwhelmed with the situation to the point that they became angry and depressed, and by virtue of circumstances, they could not walk away. I happened to fall right in the middle of these two categories. I was blessed with the ability to walk away if I wanted to and venture into other endeavors, but my love for medicine and what medicine meant to me was the main reason I couldn't walk away. In essence, I was stuck, miserable, morally fatigued, and injured with low job satisfaction and morale and heading towards work-related colloquial depression.

As I slowly descended into this dark, hollow space, then came the Covid-19 pandemic. The gravity of the impact of the pandemic on every facet of my well-being is hard to comprehend. The incessant emotional tolls of witnessing unnecessary suffering and deaths that are avoidable and the unfortunate experiencing of colleagues succumbing to the infection as collateral damage is enough to give anyone PTSD. Unfortunately, a lot of healthcare workers involved in the care of Covid patients are currently suffering through this as I type these words.

The state I was in at the time was not tenable; if I wanted to continue in the field, I had to make drastic changes. However, I was already feeling all the unintended consequences (bad dietary habits, no physical activities, lack of sleep, lackluster relationship with my wife and family, and a reclusive lifestyle) of overwhelming stress and early colloquial depression. Ironically, while I was experiencing this state, the organization I was fortunate to be affiliated with embarked on a new initiative with a focus on whole-patient care. This happened to be a blessing in disguise.

As I tried to understand the concept of this whole-person care, I recognized the predicaments I was in as a provider. On the one hand, we were trying to get patients in and out more quickly, and on the other hand, we were being told to perform whole-patient care. How do we accomplish this in an environment where speed and metrics from door to discharge are a priority? What a way to accelerate the exit of physicians already on edge. This was when it dawned on me, and I asked one of my colleagues the following question: "How does a physician that is not whole or morally injured perform whole-patient care?" Herein is the beginning of my journey.

In order for a physician to provide whole-patient care, the physician has to be whole. While I embraced the concept of whole-patient care, I wasn't whole. For me to execute this process, I had to become whole, and this was the beginning of my journey to wholeness. The thoughts and concepts in this book represent my understanding of whole-patient care and the elements of wholeness and how I applied those concepts to my strategy of becoming whole. While this was my journey, I have conducted an extensive evidence-based review on this concept, and my hope is that my road to wholeness might serve as a blueprint for others that might be facing the kind of predicament that I was experiencing (regardless of your work or life) to begin their own journey to becoming whole. For a person to be whole, they have to have a balance between all pillars (physical, emotional, mental, spiritual, and social) of wholeness.

As I continued with my journey, my organization began to recognize the importance of physician wholeness and well-being and the reality of mental health crises in medicine. Under the stewardship of the dynamic hospital leadership team with the medical staff leaders that I was part of, the institution invested in the Center for Physician Well-Being. This was a blessing that cannot be overstated. The center is staffed with experienced clinical psychologists that provide free resources to physicians as needed. As we continue to battle the Covid-19 pandemic, the resources provided by the Center for Physician Well-Being and its psychologists cannot be timelier. The emergency medicine physicians, the Covid-19 units team members, and the intensivists who are morally injured, burned out, and empathetically fatigued from caring for non-ending patients that often succumbed to the disease welcomed the resources with open arms. Additionally, these resources enabled us to adequately manage our emotions and sanity as we watched colleagues die from the disease or the overwhelming anxiety of potentially becoming the next victim. The Center for Physician Well-Being is a welcoming addition to our organization.

The most impactful aspect of the center is their understanding of our current healthcare predicaments as providers. As a result, physicians have access to free six anonymous counseling sessions per calendar year that are easily accessible either in-person or via telehealth. Several providers have utilized these resources via self-referral or encouragement by colleagues.

Additionally, understanding that physician behaviors that are unbecoming might be due to underlying and unrecognized emotional turmoil is imperative. Led by the medical staff leadership, with the support of the hospital, The Center for Physicians Professionalism was established. This has made a significant impact on the health of the medical staff. Physicians with sudden unusual behaviors that deviate from the expected norm are referred to the center via a behavioral complaint generated by observers. After an exhaustive investigation and meeting with the physician in question, a disposition is generated. Based on the disposition of the complaint, the case is either dismissed, escalated to a code of conduct, or referred to the Center for Physician Well-Being.

The majority of the physicians referred to the center were discovered to have stressors in their lives that were impacting their job performance, such as loss of loved ones, work-related stress, relationship stress, or financial stress. The plans generated by the psychologists after several meetings enabled the physicians to embark on their journey to mental and emotional wellness. This has allowed us to keep a pulse on physicians that might be suffering quietly from emotional or overwhelming stress and provide them the necessary interventions before their situations deteriorate.

As you can see from my institutional experience, the relationship between medical staff leadership and hospital administration in a collaborative fashion was able to provide these resources. By no means was this an easy feat; it took several years and iterations and leadership transitions to arrive at the right product that was embraced by all. Although the resources necessary to assist physicians on their journey to mental and emotional wellness have been made available, it is incumbent on the physicians and other healthcare workers to recognize when to push the proverbial pause button and capitalize on the available resources. While emotional wellness and mental wellness are two dimensions of my five pillars, it is imperative that physicians and other healthcare workers strive to accomplish a balance between all five pillars to be whole.

Are you ready to be whole? Are you ready to be ***fully alive by experiencing the five pillars of wholeness?*** Let the journey begin!

Well-Being Resources:

Personal Well-Being Assessment Tools:

•Wmich.edu/eup-instructional/wellbeing Assessment/

•Https://umatter.princeton.edu/sites/umatter/files/media/Princeton-umatter-wellness-self assessment.pdf

•Self-Assessment/WellMD &WellPhD/Stanford Medicine

•www.ihi.org/Engage/initiatives/100MillionHeealthierLives/Docuents/100MLives_Well-Being-Assessment_Adult.Pdf

Emotional Well-Being Tools:

•Emotional Wellness Toolkit/National Institute of Health (NIH)

•Emotional Well-being stress management solutions/HealthWell solutions

Mental Well-Being Tools:

•Warwick-Edinburgh Mental Wellbeing Scale (WEMBS)

Bibliography

Anderson, Gerard F., and Jean-Pierre Poullier. "Health Spending, Access, and Outcomes: Trends in Industrialized Countries." *Health Affairs* 18, no. 3 (1999): 178–92. https://doi.org/10.1377/hlthaff.18.3.178.

"Anti-Vaxxers, Anti-Maskers and Conspiracists: US Has Become a Melting Pot for Anti-Science 'Viruses'." Global Times, August 13, 2021. https://www.globaltimes.cn/page/202108/1231433.shtml.

Balkin, T J, Gregory Belenky, Christopher Drake, and R Rosa. "Sleep in America Poll." ResearchGate, June 2006. https://www.researchgate.net/publication/285897670_Sleep_in_America_poll_summary_of_findings.

Beccuti, Guglielmo, and Silvana Pannain. "Sleep and Obesity." *Current Opinion in Clinical Nutrition and Metabolic Care* 14, no. 4 (2011): 402–12. https://doi.org/10.1097/mco.0b013e3283479109.

Benson, Herbert, Martha M. Greenwood, and Helen Klemchuk. "The Relaxation Response: Psychophysiologic Aspects and Clinical Applications." *The International Journal of Psychiatry in Medicine* 6, no. 1-2 (1975): 87–98. https://doi.org/10.2190/376w-e4mt-qm6q-h0um.

Benson, Herbert. *The Relaxation Response*. New York: William Morrow, 1976.

Borbély, Alexander A., and Peter Achermann. "Sleep Homeostasis and Models of Sleep Regulation." *Journal of Biological Rhythms* 14, no. 6 (1999): 559–70. https://doi.org/10.1177/074873099129000894.

Bo¿ek, Agnieszka, Pawe³ F. Nowak, and Mateusz Blukacz. "The Relationship Between Spirituality, Health-Related Behavior, and Psychological Well-Being." *Frontiers in Psychology* 11 (2020). https://doi.org/10.3389/fpsyg.2020.01997.

"Brain Basics: Understanding Sleep." National Institute of Neurological Disorders and Stroke. U.S. Department of Health and Human Services, n.d. https://www.ninds.nih.gov/Disorders/patient-caregiver-education/Understanding-sleep.

Brewer, J. "Mindfulness." *Encyclopedia of Mental Health*, 2016, 144–47. https://doi.org/10.1016/b978-0-12-397045-9.00134-8.

Brown, Kirk Warren, and Richard M. Ryan. "The Benefits of Being Present: Mindfulness and Its Role in Psychological Well-Being." *Journal of Personality and Social Psychology* 84, no. 4 (2003): 822–48. https://doi.org/10.1037/0022-3514.84.4.822.

Buxton, Orfeu M., and Enrico Marcelli. "Short and Long Sleep Are Positively Associated with Obesity, Diabetes, Hypertension, and Cardiovascular Disease among Adults in the United States." *Social Science & Medicine* 71, no. 5 (2010): 1027–36. https://doi.org/10.1016/j.socscimed.2010.05.041.

Capio, Catherine M., Cindy H. Sit, and Bruce Abernethy. "Physical Well-Being." *Encyclopedia of Quality of Life and Well-Being Research*, 2014,

4805–7. https://doi.org/10.1007/978-94-007-0753-5_2166.

Chapman, Larry S. "Developing a Useful Perspective on Spiritual Health: Well-Being, Spiritual Potential and the Search for Meaning." *American Journal of Health Promotion* 1, no. 3 (1986): 31–39. https://doi.org/10.4278/0890-1171-1.3.31.

"Circadian Rhythms." National Institute of General Medical Sciences. U.S. Department of Health and Human Services, n.d. https://www.nigms.nih.gov/education/fact-sheets/Pages/circadian-rhythms.aspx.

Cohen, Sheldon, Benjamin H. Gottlieb, and Lynn G. Underwood. "Social Relationships and Health." *Social Support Measurement and Intervention*, 2000, 3–26. https://doi.org/10.1093/med:psych/9780195126709.003.0001.

Cohen, Sheldon, Drury R. Sherrod, and Margaret S. Clark. "Social Skills and the Stress-Protective Role of Social Support." *Journal of Personality and Social Psychology* 50, no. 5 (1986): 963–73. https://doi.org/10.1037/0022-3514.50.5.963.

Conner, Tamlin S., Kate L. Brookie, Aimee C. Richardson, and Maria A. Polak. "On Carrots and Curiosity: Eating Fruit and Vegetables Is Associated with Greater Flourishing in Daily Life." *British Journal of Health Psychology* 20, no. 2 (2014): 413–27. https://doi.org/10.1111/bjhp.12113.

Conversano, Ciro, Alessandro Rotondo, Elena Lensi, Olivia Della Vista, Francesca Arpone, and Mario Antonio Reda. "Optimism and Its Impact on Mental and Physical Well-Being." *Clinical Practice*

& *Epidemiology in Mental Health* 1, no. 1 (2010): 25–29. https://doi.org/10.2174/1745017901006010025.

Davis, Tchiki. "What Is Well-Being? Definition, Types, and Well-Being Skills." Psychology Today. Sussex Publishers, January 2, 2019. https://www.psychologytoday.com/us/blog/click-here-happiness/201901/what-is-well-being-definition-types-and-well-being-skills.

de Kloet, E. Ron, Melly S. Oitzl, and Marian Joëls. "Stress and Cognition: Are Corticosteroids Good or Bad Guys?" *Trends in Neurosciences* 22, no. 10 (1999): 422–26. https://doi.org/10.1016/s0166-2236(99)01438-1.

Deboer, Tom. "Sleep Homeostasis and the Circadian Clock: Do the Circadian Pacemaker and the Sleep Homeostat Influence Each Other's Functioning?" *Neurobiology of Sleep and Circadian Rhythms* 5 (2018): 68–77. https://doi.org/10.1016/j.nbscr.2018.02.003.

Dusek, Jeffery A., Hasan H. Otu, Ann L. Wohlhueter, Manoj Bhasin, Luiz F. Zerbini, Marie G. Joseph, Herbert Benson, and Towia A. Libermann. "Genomic Counter-Stress Changes Induced by the Relaxation Response." *PLoS ONE* 3, no. 7 (2008). https://doi.org/10.1371/journal.pone.0002576.

Dutheil, Frédéric, Claire Aubert, Bruno Pereira, Michael Dambrun, Fares Moustafa, Martial Mermillod, Julien S. Baker, Marion Trousselard, François-Xavier Lesage, and Valentin Navel. "Suicide among Physicians and Health-Care Workers: A Systematic Review and Meta-Analysis."

PLOS ONE 14, no. 12 (December 12, 2019). https://doi.org/10.1371/journal.pone.0226361.

Ellison, Craig W. "Spiritual Well-Being: Conceptualization and Measurement." *Journal of Psychology and Theology* 11, no. 4 (1983): 330–38. https://doi.org/10.1177/009164718301100406.

"Emotional Regulation: What Is It and Why Is It Important? - San Diego: API." Alvarado Parkway Institute, November 8, 2019. https://apibhs.com/2016/09/14/emotional-regulation-what-is-it-and-why-is-it-important.

Facher, Lev. "Unvaccinated Deaths Overwhelm Health Workers in Covid Hot Zones." STAT, August 18, 2021. https://www.statnews.com/2021/08/18/health-workers-overwhelmed-covid-deaths-among-unvaccinated/.

Fehring, R J, J F Miller, and C Shaw. "Spiritual Well-Being, Religiosity, Hope, Depression, and Other Mood States in Elderly People Coping with Cancer." Oncology Nursing Forum. U.S. National Library of Medicine, May 24, 1997. https://pubmed.ncbi.nlm.nih.gov/9159782/.

Ferron, Liz. "Emotional Well Being Definition." Insights from VITAL WorkLife, n.d. https://insights.vitalworklife.com/blog/2016/01/02/wheel-of-well-being-emotional-dimension-definition.

Fisher, John. "The Four Domains Model: Connecting Spirituality, Health and Well-Being." *Religions* 2, no. 1 (2011): 17–28. https://doi.org/10.3390/rel2010017.

Fox, Kenneth R. *The Physical Self: from Motivation to Well-Being.* Champaign, IL: Human Kinetics, 1997.

Franzen, Peter L., Peter J. Gianaros, Anna L. Marsland, Martica H. Hall, Greg J. Siegle, Ronald E. Dahl, and Daniel J. Buysse. "Cardiovascular Reactivity to Acute Psychological Stress Following Sleep Deprivation." *Psychosomatic Medicine* 73, no. 8 (2011): 679–82. https://doi.org/10.1097/psy.0b013e31822ff440.

Galderisi, Silvana, Andreas Heinz, Marianne Kastrup, Julian Beezhold, and Norman Sartorius. "Toward a New Definition of Mental Health." *World Psychiatry* 14, no. 2 (2015): 231–33. https://doi.org/10.1002/wps.20231.

Ghaderi, Ahmad, Seyed Mahmoud Tabatabaei, Saharnaz Nedjat, Mohsen Javadi, and Bagher Larijani. "Explanatory Definition of the Concept of Spiritual Health: a Qualitative Study in Iran." Journal of medical ethics and history of medicine. Tehran University of Medical Sciences, April 9, 2018. https://www.ncbi.nlm.nih.gov/pmc/articles/PMC6150917/.

"Global Strategy on Diet, Physical Activity and Health." World Health Organization, 2004. https://www.who.int/dietphysicalactivity/strategy/eb11344/strategy_english_web.pdf.

Goldstein, David S, and Irwin J Kopin. "Adrenomedullary, Adrenocortical, and Sympathoneural Responses to Stressors: a Meta-Analysis." U.S. National Library of Medicine, September 2008. https://pubmed.ncbi.nlm.nih.gov/18999898/.

Greenwood, Carol E., and Gordon Winocur. "High-Fat Diets, Insulin Resistance and Declining Cognitive Function." *Neurobiology of Aging* 26, no.

1 (2005): 42–45. https://doi.org/10.1016/j.neurobiolaging.2005.08.017.

Greenwood, Carol E., and Gordon Winocur. "High-Fat Diets, Insulin Resistance and Declining Cognitive Function." *Neurobiology of Aging* 26, no. 1 (2005): 42–45. https://doi.org/10.1016/j.neurobiolaging.2005.08.017.

Guo, Xiaofan, Liqiang Zheng, Jun Wang, Xiaoyu Zhang, Xingang Zhang, Jue Li, and Yingxian Sun. "Epidemiological Evidence for the Link between Sleep Duration and High Blood Pressure: A Systematic Review and Meta-Analysis." *Sleep Medicine* 14, no. 4 (2013): 324–32. https://doi.org/10.1016/j.sleep.2012.12.001.

Gómez-Pinilla, Fernando, and Ethika Tyagi. "Diet and Cognition." *Current Opinion in Clinical Nutrition and Metabolic Care* 16, no. 6 (2013): 726–33. https://doi.org/10.1097/mco.0b013e328365aae3.

Gómez-Pinilla, Fernando. "Brain Foods: the Effects of Nutrients on Brain Function." *Nature Reviews Neuroscience* 9, no. 7 (2008): 568–78. https://doi.org/10.1038/nrn2421.

Gómez-Pinilla, Fernando. "Brain Foods: the Effects of Nutrients on Brain Function." *Nature Reviews Neuroscience* 9, no. 7 (2008): 568–78. https://doi.org/10.1038/nrn2421.

Hafenbrack, Andrew, Zoe Kinias, and Sigal Barsade. "Debiasing the Mind through Meditation: Mindfulness and the Sunk Cost Bias." *Academy of Management Proceedings* 2013, no. 1 (2013): 11582. https://doi.org/10.5465/ambpp.2013.11582abstract.

Hakulinen, Christian, Laura Pulkki-Råback, Marianna Virtanen, Markus Jokela, Mika Kivimäki, and Marko Elovainio. "Social Isolation and Loneliness as Risk Factors for Myocardial Infarction, Stroke and Mortality: UK Biobank Cohort Study of 479 054 Men and Women." *Heart* 104, no. 18 (2018): 1536–42. https://doi.org/10.1136/heartjnl-2017-312663.

Hay, David, K. Helmut Reich, and Michael Utsch. "Spiritual Development: Intersections and Divergence with Religious Development." *The Handbook of Spiritual Development in Childhood and Adolescence*, n.d., 46–59. https://doi.org/10.4135/9781412976657.n4.

Herrman, Helen, Shekhar Saxena, and Rob Moodie. *Promoting Mental Health: Concepts, Emerging Evidence, Practice: a Report of the World Health Organization, Department of Mental Health and Substance Abuse in Collaboration with the Victorian Health Promotion Foundation and the University of Melbourne*. Geneva: World Health Organization, 2006.

Himmelstein, David U., Miraya Jun, Reinhard Busse, Karine Chevreul, Alexander Geissler, Patrick Jeurissen, Sarah Thomson, Marie-Amelie Vinet, and Steffie Woolhandler. "A Comparison of Hospital Administrative Costs in Eight Nations: US Costs Exceed All Others by Far." *Health Affairs* 33, no. 9 (September 2014): 1586–94. https://doi.org/10.1377/hlthaff.2013.1327.

"Historical NHE, 2019:" CMS.gov, 2019. https://www.cms.gov/Research-Statistics-Data-and-Systems/Statistics-Trends-and-Reports/NationalHealthExpendData/NHE-Fact-Sheet.

Holt-Lunstad, Julianne, Timothy B. Smith, Mark Baker, Tyler Harris, and David Stephenson.

"Loneliness and Social Isolation as Risk Factors for Mortality." *Perspectives on Psychological Science* 10, no. 2 (2015): 227–37. https://doi.org/10.1177/1745691614568352.

House, J., K. Landis, and D Umberson. "Social Relationships and Health." *Science* 241, no. 4865 (1988): 540–45. https://doi.org/10.1126/science.3399889.

"Improving Emotional Intelligence (EQ)." HelpGuide.org, n.d. https://www.helpguide.org/articles/mental-health/emotional-intelligence-eq.htm.

Ivancevich, J. M., M. T. Matteson, and C. Preston. "Occupational Stress, Type A Behavior, and Physical Well Being." *Academy of Management Journal* 25, no. 2 (1982): 373–91. https://doi.org/10.2307/255998.

Joëls, Marian. "Corticosteroids and the Brain." *Journal of Endocrinology* 238, no. 3 (2018). https://doi.org/10.1530/joe-18-0226.

Kalmoe, Molly C, Matthew B Chapman, Jessica A Gold, and Andrea M Giedinghagen. "Physician Suicide: A Call to Action." *PubMed* 116, no. 3 (2019): 211–16.

Kane, Leslie. "Medscape's 2020 Physician Burnout Report Finds Main Causes and Coping Mechanisms Differ by Generation." Medscape's 2020 Physician Burnout Report Finds Main Causes and Coping Mechanisms Differ by Generation, January 15, 2020. https://www.prnewswire.com/news-releases/medscapes-2020-physician-burnout-report-finds-main-causes-and-coping-mechanisms-differ-by-generation-300986764.html.

Keng, Shian-Ling, Moria J. Smoski, and Clive J. Robins. "Effects of Mindfulness on Psychological Health: A Review of Empirical Studies." *Clinical Psychology Review* 31, no. 6 (2011): 1041–56. https://doi.org/10.1016/j.cpr.2011.04.006.

Kesti, Marko, Jaana Leinonen, and Antti Syväjärvi. "A Multidisciplinary Critical Approach to Measure and Analyze Human Capital Productivity." *Advances in Human Resources Management and Organizational Development*, 2016, 1–22. https://doi.org/10.4018/978-1-4666-9652-5.ch001.

Keyes, C.L.M. "Psychological Well-Being." *Encyclopedia of Gerontology*, 2007, 399–406. https://doi.org/10.1016/b0-12-370870-2/00156-6.

Keyes, Corey Lee. "Social Well-Being." *Social Psychology Quarterly* 61, no. 2 (1998): 121. https://doi.org/10.2307/2787065.

Khullar, Dhruv. "Treating the Unvaccinated." The New Yorker, July 16, 2021. https://www.newyorker.com/science/medical-dispatch/treating-the-unvaccinated.

Kingston, Amanda M. "Break the Silence: Physician Suicide in the Time of COVID-19." *PubMed* 117, no. 5 (2020): 426–29.

Mateo, Jill M. "Inverted-U Shape Relationship between Cortisol and Learning in Ground Squirrels." *Neurobiology of Learning and Memory* 89, no. 4 (2008): 582–90. https://doi.org/10.1016/j.nlm.2007.11.002.

McCann, Joyce C, and Bruce N Ames. "Is Docosahexaenoic Acid, an n"3 Long-Chain Polyunsaturated Fatty Acid, Required for Development of Normal Brain Function? An

Overview of Evidence from Cognitive and Behavioral Tests in Humans and Animals." *The American Journal of Clinical Nutrition* 82, no. 2 (2005): 281–95. https://doi.org/10.1093/ajcn/82.2.281.

Motomura, Yuki, Ruri Katsunuma, Michitaka Yoshimura, and Kazuo Mishima. "Two Days' Sleep Debt Causes Mood Decline during Resting State via Diminished Amygdala-Prefrontal Connectivity." *Sleep*, 2017. https://doi.org/10.1093/sleep/zsx133.

Moutier, Christine Yu, Michael F. Myers, Jennifer Breen Feist, J. Corey Feist, and Sidney Zisook. "Preventing Clinician Suicide: A Call to Action during the COVID-19 Pandemic and Beyond." *Academic Medicine* 96, no. 5 (May 1, 2021): 624–28. https://doi.org/10.1097/acm.0000000000003972.

Muccioli, Giampiero, Matthias Tschöp, Mauro Papotti, Romano Deghenghi, Mark Heiman, and Ezio Ghigo. "Neuroendocrine and Peripheral Activities of Ghrelin: Implications in Metabolism and Obesity." *European Journal of Pharmacology* 440, no. 2-3 (2002): 235–54. https://doi.org/10.1016/s0014-2999(02)01432-2.

Nolan, Peter, and Paul Crawford. "Towards a Rhetoric of Spirituality in Mental Health Care." *Journal of Advanced Nursing* 26, no. 2 (1997): 289–94. https://doi.org/10.1046/j.1365-2648.1997.1997026289.x.

Nunner, Matteo. "Medscape National Physician Burnout & Depression Report 2018." MedicinaNarrativa.eu, February 23, 2018. https://www.medicinanarrativa.eu/medscape-national-physician-burnout-depression-report-2018.

O'Donnell, Jayne. "Huge Health Care Price Differences Even within Same Area, by State." *USA Today.* April 27, 2016.

Oja, Pekka, and Sylvia Titze. "Physical Activity Recommendations for Public Health: Development and Policy Context." *EPMA Journal* 2, no. 3 (2011): 253–59. https://doi.org/10.1007/s13167-011-0090-1.

Oldnall, Andrew. "A Critical Analysis of Nursing: Meeting the Spiritual Needs of Patients." *Journal of Advanced Nursing* 23, no. 1 (1996): 138–44. https://doi.org/10.1111/j.1365-2648.1996.tb03145.x.

Pate, R. R. "Physical Activity and Public Health. A Recommendation from the Centers for Disease Control and Prevention and the American College of Sports Medicine." *JAMA: The Journal of the American Medical Association* 273, no. 5 (1995): 402–7. https://doi.org/10.1001/jama.273.5.402.

Pedisic, Zeljko, Nipun Shrestha, Stephanie Kovalchik, Emmanuel Stamatakis, Nucharapon Liangruenrom, Jozo Grgic, Sylvia Titze, Stuart JH Biddle, Adrian E Bauman, and Pekka Oja. "Is Running Associated with a Lower Risk of All-Cause, Cardiovascular and Cancer Mortality, and Is the More the Better? A Systematic Review and Meta-Analysis." *British Journal of Sports Medicine* 54, no. 15 (2019): 898–905. https://doi.org/10.1136/bjsports-2018-100493.

Priestley, Jack G. "Towards Finding the Hidden Curriculum: A Consideration of the Spiritual Dimension of Experience in Curriculum Planning." *British Journal of Religious Education* 7, no. 3

(1985): 112–19. https://doi.org/10.1080/0141620840070303.

Ranabir, Salam, and K Reetu. "Stress and Hormones." *Indian Journal of Endocrinology and Metabolism* 15, no. 1 (2011): 18. https://doi.org/10.4103/2230-8210.77573.

Rash, Joshua A., M. Kyle Matsuba, and Kenneth M. Prkachin. "Gratitude and Well-Being: Who Benefits the Most from a Gratitude Intervention?" *Applied Psychology: Health and Well-Being* 3, no. 3 (2011): 350–69. https://doi.org/10.1111/j.1758-0854.2011.01058.x.

Reichert, Carolin, Micheline Maire, Christina Schmidt, and Christian Cajochen. "Sleep-Wake Regulation and Its Impact on Working Memory Performance: The Role of Adenosine." *Biology* 5, no. 1 (2016): 11. https://doi.org/10.3390/biology5010011.

Reith, Thomas P. "Burnout in United States Healthcare Professionals: A Narrative Review." *Cureus* 10, no. 12 (December 4, 2018). https://doi.org/10.7759/cureus.3681.

Robinson, Lawrence. "Relaxation Techniques for Stress Relief." HelpGuide.org, n.d. https://www.helpguide.org/articles/stress/relaxation-techniques-for-stress-relief.htm.

Rotenstein, Lisa S., Matthew Torre, Marco A. Ramos, Rachael C. Rosales, Constance Guille, Srijan Sen, and Douglas A. Mata. "Prevalence of Burnout among Physicians: A Systematic Review." *JAMA* 320, no. 11 (September 18, 2018): 1131–50. https://doi.org/10.1001/jama.2018.12777.

Saghir, Zahid, Javeria N. Syeda, Adnan S. Muhammad, and Tareg H. Balla Abdalla. "The

Amygdala, Sleep Debt, Sleep Deprivation, and the Emotion of Anger: A Possible Connection?" Cureus, July 2, 2018. https://www.cureus.com/articles/13022-the-amygdala-sleep-debt-sleep-deprivation-and-the-emotion-of-anger-a-possible-connection.

Schernhammer, Eva S., and Graham A. Colditz. "Suicide Rates among Physicians: A Quantitative and Gender Assessment (Meta-Analysis)." *American Journal of Psychiatry* 161, no. 12 (December 1, 2004): 2295–2302. https://doi.org/10.1176/appi.ajp.161.12.2295.

Schieber, George J. "Health Expenditures in Major Industrialized Countries, 1960-87." *Health Care Financing Review* 11, no. 4 (1990): 159–67.

Sellers, Frances Stead, Ariana Eunjung Cha, Hannah Knowles, and Derek Hawkins. "The Delta Variant Is Putting America's Hospitals Back in Crisis Mode." The Washington Post. WP Company, August 18, 2021. https://www.washingtonpost.com/health/2021/08/18/covid-hospitals-delta/.

Shlisky, Julie D., Terryl J. Hartman, Penny M. Kris-Etherton, Connie J. Rogers, Neil A. Sharkey, and Sharon M. Nickols-Richardson. "Partial Sleep Deprivation and Energy Balance in Adults: An Emerging Issue for Consideration by Dietetics Practitioners." *Journal of the Academy of Nutrition and Dietetics* 112, no. 11 (2012): 1785–97. https://doi.org/10.1016/j.jand.2012.07.032.

Short, Michelle A., and Mia Louca. "Sleep Deprivation Leads to Mood Deficits in Healthy Adolescents." *Sleep Medicine* 16, no. 8 (2015): 987–93. https://doi.org/10.1016/j.sleep.2015.03.007.

Sirven, Nicolas, and Thierry Debrand. "Social Participation and Healthy Ageing: An International

Comparison Using SHARE Data." *Social Science & Medicine* 67, no. 12 (2008): 2017–26. https://doi.org/10.1016/j.socscimed.2008.09.056.

Smith, Michael A. "We Don't Owe the Unvaccinated Priority on Hospital Care." The Daily News, August 14, 2021. https://www.galvnews.com/opinion/editorials/free/article_218a58d6-9417-5731-ae60-c1010b819393.html.

Spiegel, Karine, Esra Tasali, Plamen Penev, and Eve Van Cauter. "Brief Communication: Sleep Curtailment in Healthy Young Men Is Associated with Decreased Leptin Levels, Elevated Ghrelin Levels, and Increased Hunger and Appetite." *Annals of Internal Medicine* 141, no. 11 (2004): 846. https://doi.org/10.7326/0003-4819-141-11-200412070-00008.

Srivastava, Ritika. "Spiritual Wellbeing at Work: How to Do It Right." HRZone, September 19, 2019. https://www.hrzone.com/lead/culture/spiritual-wellbeing-at-work-how-to-do-it-right.

Staff, Mindful, Mindful Staff, Peter Jaret, Parneet Pal, Kristin Fitzgerald-Zita, Stephanie Domet, Christopher Willard, Michelle Maldonado, Elisha Goldstein, and Caren Osten Gerszberg. "What Is Mindfulness?" Mindful, February 18, 2021. https://www.mindful.org/what-is-mindfulness/.

"Stress in America Key Findings: 2010." American Psychological Association, 2010. https://www.apa.org/news/press/releases/stress/2010/key-findings.

Tennant, Ruth, Louise Hiller, Ruth Fishwick, Stephen Platt, Stephen Joseph, Scott Weich, Jane Parkinson, Jenny Secker, and Sarah Stewart-

Brown. "The Warwick-Edinburgh Mental Well-Being Scale (WEMWBS): Development and UK Validation." *Health and Quality of Life Outcomes* 5, no. 1 (2007): 63. https://doi.org/10.1186/1477-7525-5-63.

Valtorta, Nicole K, Mona Kanaan, Simon Gilbody, Sara Ronzi, and Barbara Hanratty. "Loneliness and Social Isolation as Risk Factors for Coronary Heart Disease and Stroke: Systematic Review and Meta-Analysis of Longitudinal Observational Studies." *Heart* 102, no. 13 (2016): 1009–16. https://doi.org/10.1136/heartjnl-2015-308790.

Wanjek, Christopher. "Food at Work: Workplace Solutions for Malnutrition, Obesity and Chronic Diseases." International Labor Organization, June 10, 2005. https://www.ilo.org/global/publications/ilo-bookstore/order-online/books/WCMS_PUBL_9221170152_EN/lang—en/index.htm.

Warburton, D. E.R. "Health Benefits of Physical Activity: the Evidence." *Canadian Medical Association Journal* 174, no. 6 (2006): 801–9. https://doi.org/10.1503/cmaj.051351.

Wheeler, Philippa. "Spirituality & Health Multidisciplinary Explorations. Edited by Augustine Meier and Thomas St. James O'Connor. Waterloo, Ontario: Wilfrid Laurier University Press, 2005, ISBN 0-88920-477-2." *Spirituality and Health International* 8, no. 4 (2007): 225–27. https://doi.org/10.1002/shi.320.

Wynn-Jones, W., T. P. Koehlmoos, C. Tompkins, A. Navathe, S. Lipsitz, N. K. Kwon, P. A. Learn, C. Madsen, A. Schoenfeld, and J. S. Weissman. "Variation in Expenditure for Common, High Cost Surgical Procedures in a Working Age Population:

Implications for Reimbursement Reform." *BMC Health Services Research* 19, no. 877 (November 21, 2019). https://doi.org/10.1186/s12913-019-4729-2.

Yerkes, Robert M., and John D. Dodson. "The Relation of Strength of Stimulus to Rapidity of Habit-Formation." *Journal of Comparative Neurology and Psychology* 18, no. 5 (1908): 459–82. https://doi.org/10.1002/cne.920180503.

Zimberg, Ioná Zalcman, Ana Dâmaso, Mariana Del Re, Aline Millani Carneiro, Helton Sá Souza, Fábio Santos Lira, Sergio Tufik, and Marco Túlio Mello. "Short Sleep Duration and Obesity: Mechanisms and Future Perspectives." *Cell Biochemistry and Function* 30, no. 6 (2012): 524–29. https://doi.org/10.1002/cbf.283

About the Author

Dr. Ademola Adewale is a board-certified Emergency Medicine Physician with over twenty years of practice experience. He completed his medical education at Howard University College of Medicine and his Emergency Medicine specialty training at Drexel University College of Medicine/ Allegheny General Hospital in Pittsburgh, PA. He is the co-founder of the Emergency Medicine residency training program at the AdventHealth System in East Orlando, Florida. He served as the Director of Research, Director of Simulation, Residents Wellness Champion, and the Assistant Program Director for the residency program for over a decade. He currently serves as faculty advisor and the Medical Director for the Center for Medical Simulation and Education at AdventHealth East Orlando.

He is an accomplished medical staff leader who is involved in the paradigm shift of holding physicians accountable. He completed the AdventHealth Physician Leadership Development Program, an institutionally designed program that serves as an incubator for physician leaders. He is involved in several committees in the hospital. He has served in the role of Chief of Staff and currently serving as the President-Elect of the Medical Staff of the Central Florida Division of AdventHealth Hospital system.

Dr. Adewale is a consummate advocate for residents' wellness. His passion for physician wellness started over a decade ago with the identification of increasing resident burnout. The search for a solution to this problem led to the development of a wellness program for the Emergency Medicine residents. This passion was cemented when healthcare institutions were promoting the concept of "Whole-Patient Care" despite increasing physicians' burnout, depression, and suicides. His understanding of the impracticality of burned-out physicians performing whole-patient care prompted his research into how a physician could become whole. This was predicated on the theory that a physician that is not whole, depressed, or burned-out, cannot perform whole-patient care. The culmination of his research is the context of this book.